December 7, 1941 will forever be a traumatic, tragic, and enigmatic date to Americans. Just how was our Pacific fleet at Pearl Harbor so completely surprised by the treacherous Japanese attack?

In Washington that day, while the attack was underway, Japanese diplomats were still at their task of deceiving our government that lasting peace between the two nations was assured or at least possible.

Frank Schuler is one of the few living foreign service officers who had inside and firsthand information on Japanese relations during the nine years leading up to the attack at Pearl Harbor. Two years ago Frank came to me with his story.

The unwritten operating code of the State Department back then decreed absolute secrecy, even cover-up, for foreign service blundering. Schuler lived with this suppressed information for thirty-three years; but now, with the code of behavior changed and most of the participants passed from the scene, Frank feels compelled to reveal his story.

Frank Schuler and I both hope this book will destroy the lies and myths perpetrated by the detractors of President Franklin D. Roosevelt. Incredibly, they claim that FDR knew the attack was coming and allowed it to crash down on our unsuspecting army and navy forces at Pearl Harbor in order to shock America into war in Europe!

We also trust that the new information in this book will contribute to a fresh understanding of the roles played by all who were in positions of power during the years before and after Pearl Harbor . . . and, lastly, that this book will now persuade others to come forth and finally complete the historical perspectives so long misstated and misunderstood.

—Robin Moore
Westport, Conn.
June 1976

THE PEARL HARBOR COVER-UP

by Frank Schuler
and
Robin Moore

PINNACLE BOOKS   NEW YORK CITY

This is a work of fiction *and* nonfiction. Several of the
characters and scenes portrayed in this book are fictional,
and any resemblance to real people and incidents is purely
coincidental. Please note further amplification in the
authors' Preface and Introduction.

THE PEARL HARBOR COVER-UP

Copyright © 1976 by Maurice J. Day

An original Pinnacle Books edition, published for the first
time anywhere.

ISBN: 0-523-00983-6

First printing, September 1976
Second printing, January 1977

Printed in the United States of America

PINNACLE BOOKS, INC.
275 Madison Avenue
New York, N.Y. 10016

PREFACE
(The Pearl Harbor Cover-Up)

The Pearl Harbor Cover-Up is an exposé of gross negligence, near criminal oversight, and a tragic display of ugly megalomania on the part of Joseph C. Grew, Ambassador to Japan during the pre-World War Two period, and some of the individuals close to him in the Department of State. Despite the enormity of their failings, there is a more ominous and onerous extension that only compounds their guilt, because, in a deviously planned and coordinated effort, Grew and his lackeys formulated a scheme to expunge Department of State records and files in order to delete evidence that would have factually pointed a condemning finger at the people actually responsible for the horror of the sneak attack on Pearl Harbor.

The cover-up is an adventure that has been hidden over the years—and a misadventure that has allowed blame for the gargantuan losses to rest on the memory of President Franklin Delano Roosevelt and, to a lesser extent, his Secretary of State, Cordell Hull.

When, on December 8, 1941, FDR talked to the nation of ". . . a date which will live in infamy . . ." he might also have been privately contemplating the infamous blunderings of his Ambassador to Japan, which led to a virtually incalculable loss of life, power, and international prestige. That the attack on Pearl Harbor welded the American people together in their resolve to fight totalitarianism is a matter of historical fact; that the devastation could have been lessened—even avoided—will be examined in this effort by one of the men who lived through the nightmare.

Frank A. Schuler, Jr. served with the Department of State's Foreign Service from 1930 until 1953 and, subsequently has been involved in various governmental capacities. His presence in State was a burden—even a danger—to the Pearl Harbor cover-up because he was privy to events as they actually occurred. As a result, his life for years was a living hell of frustration and denigration perpetrated by Grew and propagated by Grew's departmental staff. But this is not Frank Schuler's story; it is the product of his personal experiences, particular knowledge, and dogged devotion to truth. Here is an epic which, for sundry reasons, has missed its proper niche in history.

THE PEARL HARBOR COVER-UP

INTRODUCTION

The premise of this work is based on authenti-
cated information, documents and newly revealed
historical facts. Prior to the tragedy of Pearl
Harbor, there was a clique within the Department of State that performed their duties in such
a manner that, in the light of history, they appear to be guilty of culpable negligence. Subsequently, in order to cover their misdeeds, they un-
dertook actions which, by their nature, condemn
the participants of criminal conspiracy and falsi-
fication of documents.

This book is one of the new products of con-
temporary journalism, a category that the book
industry has broadly labeled "faction"—a blend
of fact and fiction. Truman Capote and the team
of Woodward & Bernstein are probably (along
with me) the foremost practitioners of this form.
So, just as an artist might add a tree to a barren
landscape, the authors of this book have added
characters who did not exist but who are, in fact,
composites of several individuals involved in this
piece of history. Likewise, as an object might be

moved in a painting for the benefit of composition, so too, have some incidents and actions been rearranged within a time frame that the authors feel is acceptable within the concept of fictionalizing history in order to make it more readable and informative—but no less true.

The guiding premise of the authors has been that nothing described herein is to be misleading or misguiding in that—to their personal knowledge, from extensive research and thorough documentation—every incident did occur or could have happened.

The reader should not be offended if some names of individuals have been changed; this device has been used merely out of respect for the sensitivities of those innocent few living persons who remain in the wake of The Pearl Harbor Cover-Up.

R.M.

Part One

CHAPTER 1

KYOTO, JAPAN

AUGUST 11, 1941

Ken Reynolds untangled his legs from their contorted position and stretched them in front of him. He listened in painful relief as his flannel trousers scratched noisily against the grain of the *tatami* underneath him. The tightly woven straw mat slid slightly on the hard lacquered floor and he stopped moving.

Shizuko stood a few feet away from Ken and smiled. In her lovely, sing-song lilt, she said, "You soon rearn, Ken-san." He had known her for a month and was still charmed by her native inability to pronounce an *l*.

"I doubt," he said slowly so she could translate the thought in her mind. He would have added that he saw no sense in the Japanese custom of floor sitting but that would have required a long discussion and it might also have offended her.

She politely nodded her faint understanding and slid back the *shoji*, a latticework door frame covered with thin rice paper. Her heavy *tabi* socks slid gracefully through the doorway and she flowed silently out of the room. As she eased the door shut, he looked at her as he had a thousand times before and felt the surge of desire that had become so familiar to him. Even though she was clothed from neck to toes in her expensive kimono, she was as sensual as anyone he had ever seen: her tiny breasts accented by the *juban* collar; the flowing drape of the material over her waist; the slight mound of her bottom curving out under the *obi* on her back. All of these teasing suggestions made Shizuko urgently desirable to him, yet he happily restrained his physical urge to take her: The ritual of waiting was almost as rewarding as the final copulation.

He completed his stretch as she closed the door and waited as she went to get the equipment necessary for the symbolic tea ceremony she would prepare before they could come together.

He had come to know Shizuko Tokushima casually, then had found the acquaintance useful.

Lieutenant Ken Reynolds, USN, Annapolis, Class of '36, agent for the Office of Naval Intelligence, was in Japan with a deep cover—working as a marketing representative for the Parks Toy Company. According to his cover, Ken Reynolds was negotiating with several major Japanese toy manufacturers to distribute their products in the United States under the famous Parks trademark. Of course, the oil and trade embargo had been a deterrent, and, just over two weeks before the U.S. government's freezing of Japanese assets in America had just about completely undermined Ken's alleged purpose for being in Japan. Still, much to his pleasure, one of the manufacturers in nearby Kobe was still willing to talk, probably at the suggestion of the Imperial Cabinet's Foreign Office, acting under the pretense

4

that there was still hope for a peaceful solution to international problems.

For nearly seven months, Ken had been able to move in the high levels of the Japanese *zaibatsu*, the monopoly industries of the Empire. Because he came to them with impressive—though false—credentials, he was feted well and was able to travel with only a modicum of restrictions. Shizuko Tokushima came into the undercover agent's life at a business dinner in Osaka, when a submanager of the famous Korii Toy Company hosted Ken to a geisha evening.

She had, quite properly, been distant during the early part of the evening, granting him only slight attention as the five girls worked the small party in rotation. But she was the only geisha there who knew a few words of English and, because Ken knew only a smattering of kitchen Japanese, the host made the necessary suggestions that encouraged Shizuko to concentrate on the American guest. There was a chemistry between the two, and, as the party drew to a close and the males were beginning to choose partners for what might come later, Ken's host took him aside and made it clear that Shizuko might be receptive to continuing with him. Ken accepted the possibility with grace. He knew that such an offer from an accomplished geisha was not automatic; the girl was traditionally allowed to accept or reject a proposal, depending on her own feelings about the male.

Ken and Shizuko spent the night together at the house of one of her geisha friends. When he found out that she had been brought from Kyoto especially for this particular party, his agent's survival antennae began to quiver; he wondered if she had been a plant of the Kempei, the dreaded military police.

Throughout that first night, he had guarded his words, drinking a full draught of her pleasures. Although he consumed the considerable amount of sake and sashimi expected of a proper guest, Ken managed to stay awake through the entire evening by talking and enjoying Shizuko's sexual skills.

It was approaching dawn when they first began discussing politics. Ken had slipped into the conversation before he realized what was going on. It was a full hour before he was able to convince himself that the geisha was not merely play-acting, and that she really had a strong, personal conviction that the growing animosity between Japan and the United States was a bad thing for both countries.

Back when Ken had been instructed at the Office of Naval Intelligence School in Washington, one ploy suggested by his instructors had been to take a strong anti-war position if an opportunity arose. He had tried the tactic three times before but met with no success. It worked on Shizuko.

After much fencing with delicate phrases, Ken determined that she had definite anti-war feelings. A geisha in Japan is privy to many sources of information, mainly because she is taught from childhood that what she hears is none of her business. While Shizuko's home in Kyoto was not a hotbed of military or industrial activity, she might be a source of intelligence.

Shizuko was convinced that Ken belonged to that class of Americans who were not only anti-war, but also pro-Japanese. They spent the next three nights together, affirming their affection and, not accidentally, arriving at the conclusion

6

that they might be able to act for the benefit of both their countries.

For the sake of appearances, Ken was forced to continue his meetings with various Japanese toy manufacturers, but as soon as he could force a break in his crowded schedule, he would barrel back down to Kyoto and snatch as much time as possible with Shizuko.

During his absences she was not idle. She had many important clients and friends who professed a similar anti-war feeling and she used them to Ken's advantage. Before long she was a pipeline of information from many sources to Ken. The feeling on the Japanese side was that Ken might use his high connections to get the American government to advance the cause of peace by improving relations with the Imperial government. In a matter of weeks, Ken was receiving vital military intelligence which he relayed to the Naval Attaché in Tokyo.

The American's liaison with the geisha did not go unnoticed by the Imperial War Department's intelligence: Soon a close watch was placed on Shizuko. When Japanese agents discovered that she had been given physical evidence of the Imperial Navy's combat exercises on Kyushu, exercises in preparation for the attack on Pearl Harbor, a quick command decision was made to close the pipeline off.

Shizuko had no way of knowing this as she came back into her room bearing the small tray. As with the tea ceremony, her information relaying had been integrated into their love-making ritual. That was fine with Ken: Spying was a nasty enough business and so mixing it with a moderate amount of romance did not seem inappropriate.

7

The *chanoyu*—tea ritual—had been performed in the customary time frame and the sensual act of unwinding her *obi* had been accomplished with the expected results: Ken was thinking more about her body than her military information.

In the faint glow of candlelight, Ken studied her body as her fingers flitted over his meager clothing. Her breasts were petite buds but so well proportioned to her small body that there was no hint of boyishness.

He savored the fragile details of her eyes, cheeks, nose, and lips ... her tongue dancing on her perfect teeth, and her huge, brown eyes. The softness of her breasts cushioned slowly down onto his chest, her flat stomach melted against his. . . .

Later, she snuggled closely to him. There was no sex play during these intermissions; if he made even the slightest move to fondle her breasts, she would coyly divert his attempts. It was during these pauses that she talked; these were the moments she would introduce information into part of their sex ritual.

"Ken-san," she whispered with hot breath against his ear.

All he could get out was a weak, "Hummmm?"

"Do we do good?" Her voice was still a hushed whisper.

He knew he was being unprofessional; he knew he should be fighting his erotic urges in order to find out if she had any new data. But these times had been productive for him and he could not always act like a spy with this woman: He was aware that he had fallen deeply in love with her.

During these pauses—that's the only word Ken could put to these deliciously torturous interludes—he had learned about the Japanese Army's

8

T-28 medium tank and the fact that it had only a 40-mile operation range, a critical piece of intelligence he had relayed to the Embassy in Tokyo. He had also learned about the fantastic capability of the Mitsubishi Zero and that piece of information had already found its way to the drawing boards of U.S. fighter plane designers at Grumman and Sikorsky. So, recognizing her need to perform this way, he suffered through the agony of waiting while hearing critical intelligence.

He listened as she spoke. To a person not knowing the language, the words would have sounded like pillow-talk because of the soft, sensual tone of her voice. "We heard," she was saying, "of a Naval operation by the fleet off Ushibuka."

The sentence came through Ken's mental haze and pricked his attention: Ushibuka was in southern Kyushu and far from any possible observation by non-Japanese. An Occidental traveling there would be spotted immediately.

Shizuko sensed him tensing and asked, "Is that of importance?"

"There is not much news available to Westerners out of Kyushu nowadays," he explained. He also had to explain *nowadays* to her.

"I rike that word," she said playfully.

With considerable effort, he suppressed his lust and, in a voice that showed little passion, asked, "What kind of naval operations?"

"Ohhh," she whined impishly.

Her body moved like a fast-traveling snake and, before he could demand a reply to his question, he felt himself engulfed again, trapped again in Shizuko's unfailing grip.

"Shi-chan," he begged, using the family familiar she allowed him to use as a sign of their closeness. He whispered her name again, pleading for her to stop and talk again.

"Please," he said, raising his voice slightly. He could see her lovely eyes staring at him. To her this was all part of making their union more intriguing, more appealing.

Looking at him, she asked, "Have you ever heard of Per Haba?"

At first, the conflict of *r*'s and *l*'s made the words hard to understand, then they crashed in on him: Pearl Harbor!

At that instant, just as his fingers went to touch her hair, there was a sound. A metallic, scraping sound. Shizuko bolted up. Fear, panic, horror, all flooded onto that lovely face. Her hand darted for the housecoat she kept on the small *kotaku* table by their mat, but she did not reach it before the door burst open.

Shizuko shouted something in Japanese that Ken could not understand; nor did he understand the words spoken by the huge man now looming in the doorway.

Three men plunged into the room, all dressed in dark uniforms. None wore insignia of any kind.

It happened so fast it seemed like a black blur to Ken's eyes. The first man in ran at him and delivered a stunning boot kick to the side of Ken's head. The flash that comes from such a blow erupted in Ken's eyes. The next thing he knew, his assailant was behind him, locking one arm back painfully and holding onto his hair with the other hand.

At the far end of the mat, Shizuko had tried to leap to her feet but was grabbed roughly by the second and largest man, a good two hundred pounds of muscle. Her attacker flung his arm widely around, pinning her arms tight against her body. Ken tried to twist free, but his captor clamped down tighter and yanked at his head.

Ken looked at Shizuko. Her body was twisting furiously, her legs kicking out trying to do damage, but the grip on her body was too strong. Suddenly, Ken saw the sparkling flash of a thin steel wire in the hand of the third man. Before he could register the fear of what might happen, the wire was coiled around Shizuko's neck. With one strong movement, the wire was twisted, then yanked in a slashing motion that cut a half-moon path across that smooth, lovely throat. Ken felt bile rushing up into his mouth as he saw the gash.

The man pulled the garotte free and Shizuko fell to the floor.

Ken looked at her, searching for the doll-like beauty that had been so much a part of her. All he could see was a mouth twisted in agony and eyes burning with pain.

The attacker spun around and took two steps to where Ken was pinned to the mat. The steel wire flew out and Ken died with a scream trapped in his throat.

CHAPTER 2

TOKYO, JAPAN

AUGUST 11, 1941

Ben Stockton walked into the Code Room on the second floor of the Embassy in Tokyo and began flipping through the messages that had come in during the night. There was nothing significant.

He turned to the young State Department code clerk and asked, "Anything in the hopper?"

Bill Roberts sipped his coffee and replied with a cynicism beyond his years, "No, sir. We had two in a gray code about midnight, but they were only logistics stuff; they're shipping some supplies from 'Frisco and administration in Washington wants all of us to begin using only Underwood ribbons in our typewriters."

Ben Stockton laughed. "Top Priority. Right?"

The code clerk smiled broadly and answered, "You'd think the most important thing in the whole diplomatic world was which typewriter ribbon to use."

"Anything exciting going on?" Stockton asked as he crossed the room and scanned the material that had come in the diplomatic pouch on Saturday. He had looked at it all the day before, but he went through it again out of habit.

Stockton's long frame registered impatience. Eyes the color of Toledo steel fixed on the papers as though they could bore through them. Many times those eyes had drilled along the barrel of a Browning a thousand feet over the trenches of the Western Front. Stockton's few months in the Lafayette Escadrille at the end of the last war had covered him in glory, but his colleagues in State were not certain that had been the best training for a diplomat. Nor was Stockton quite sure himself. The reflexes that had wiped two dozen German fighters from the Flemish sky could not always be slowed down to the snail's pace considered *de rigueur* in the Foreign Service.

Ben Stockton had been in the Tokyo Embassy for three weeks, supposedly filling the vacant square in the personnel roster created by the absence of Counselor Eugene Dooman, who was on annual leave back in the States.

Stockton was plugging a hole in the Third Secretary level, but that was purely for show; what guise he was under in Tokyo didn't matter. He had to be in that post at that particular time.

In the pre-Pearl Harbor State Department, there was a small cadre of specialists who moved from Embassy to Embassy on specific assignments dealing with whatever crises needed expert attention. Ben Stockton was one of them. The cadre was hardly the product of forward thinking by such notable State Department leaders as Secretary of State Cordell Hull or the deeply entrenched old-timers who lived by the rigid codes of diplomatic protocol. The group had been formed on the initiative of President Roosevelt, prompted by the rapidly advancing Undersecretary, Sumner Welles. Reluctantly, Secretary Hull had accepted the innovation after the President's strong insistence. Hull had acquiesced, with the proviso that the "brigands,"as he referred to the new men, did not attack the fiber of the State Department. Hull's reluctance was in keeping with his personality; he was of the Stimson school which contended with disgust: "Gentlemen do not read other people's mail." That had been in response to the news that the U.S. intelligence services had found a way to break foreign diplomatic codes, an innovation which Hull found abhorrent to his old, Tennessean code of ethics. But the group was formed and scattered out on various assignments; still, however, bound to report their information through established chains of command within the Department of State. While they added a new dimension to the Department, frequently they worked for naught when Secretary Hull interposed his influential presence in the path of the "brigands' " research and discoveries.

Ben Stockton had been sent to the Tokyo Embassy to observe the Japanese reaction to the high-level Atlantic Charter meeting between President Roosevelt and Prime Minister Churchill. No one in Tokyo knew why he was on the scene. Not even Ambassador Joseph Grew had been forewarned about the conference then being held in utmost secrecy on the battleship H.M.S. *Prince of Wales* and the cruiser U.S.S. *Augusta* at anchor in Placentia Bay off Newfoundland. Ambassador Grew had bristled when Ben had arrived in Tokyo, but then, Ambassador Grew bristled at virtually everything that did not fit within his own stringent boundaries of protocol. Stockton had "intruded" into Grew's domain three times before and on each occasion had dealt with incidents which the Ambassador felt he could have handled much better without assistance.

"My dear sir," Grew had said when Ben arrived on his most recent assignment, "I assume we will coordinate your activities better than the last time. I have made no secret that I find your presence almost intolerable. I have made this known in several circles."

Ben knew Grew had been brazen enough even to approach President Roosevelt with his complaints about "this incredible person looking over my shoulders." But the President had nodded patiently in his equable way, then pulled the conversation back to his favorite pastime—stamp collecting. When Ben had been dispatched from Washington, he had been told to treat Grew delicately, so he had been cautious.

Replying to Grew at their first encounter, Ben had said, "I understand, Mr. Ambassador. I will be extremely careful about maintaining my liaison with you. The Department has taken no issue with you, sir. I am here on only a minor assignment."

"And that is . . . ?" Grew probed.

"I can't say, sir."

The tic in the Ambassador's neck began flexing. Grew flushed with rage. "You, young man, are not only insolent; you are rude beyond the point of annoyance. I'll not have. . . ."

Ben jumped in. "I mean no offense, Mr. Ambassador. We are, sir, all on the same side."

Grew was flustered. His mouth had pulsed and his mustache resembled a miniature porcupine arming its quills for attack.

Ben smiled to himself as he finished going through the papers that had come in the despatch pouch. Their meeting had ended unpleasantly, and he had not seen the Ambassador in the three

15

weeks since. The code clerk got his attention with a casual comment: "The sailors seem to have a flap going," he said.

The offhand tone was characteristic of Embassy gossip, but it got Ben's attention, because any time the Naval Attaché was in trouble in Japan, that was important.

"How's that, Roberts?" Ben asked.

The code clerk lit a cigarette and settled back to enjoy the gossiping. "Oh," he began, "about dawn this morning, a call came to the switchboard. It was a Japanese who said: 'Keep your sailors out of Kyoto,' or something like that."

"And . . . ?"

"And, about an hour ago, the shit hit the fan. Mack Priest has the duty today and when he came in, he relayed the message to Smith-Hutton. Since then . . . well, they've been busy as hell. Gruenwald even came up and sent off a top Code to ONI in Washington. It was too hot for me to do; he encoded himself."

Ben Stockton's alarm bells began to jangle. Gruenwald was a Navy lieutenant whom Ben knew was ONI's top man in Tokyo. If he and the Naval Attaché, Lt. Comdr. Henri H. Smith-Hutton, were in on something, it might be of critical importance.

Ben moved quickly toward the door and sent back a "See you later" to the code clerk. He hurried down the hallway to the duty officer's room at the far end of the building. He heard his own feet announcing his arrival on the highly polished floor, so he was not surprised when he stuck his head in the door and saw Priest shaking his head arrogantly.

"Hey, good morning," Stockton offered.

"It's none of your business," Priest said with a heavy inflection of offense in his voice.

"Look, you shit," Ben spit out, "I don't like being here any more than you like me. But I've got a job to do and, unless you'd like to pick up your retirement check in Bangkok, get off my ass. Now where's Smith-Hutton?"

"Gone," Priest said, not mellowing his tone. "Left the compound about a half-hour ago."

"What about Gruenwald?"

Priest paused for a moment; he was worried that Stockton might have already learned about the ONI involvement. Finally, he said, "He's in Williams' office."

"Thanks," Stockton said as he spun himself away from the door. Priest said something he did not hear and he did not care to hear; Mack Priest was one of those career types who got in his way. He was glad to be out of the man's obnoxious presence.

The stairwell down to the first floor was in the middle of the building. Stockton was moving fast by the time he reached the wide circular stairs. He took the steps three at a time, almost losing his footing on the polished marble as he neared the ground floor.

"Easy, sir," the immaculately groomed Marine guard at the entrance joked as Ben angled off to the right toward the Commercial Attaché's office.

"I'll make it," Stockton quipped. He braked as he came to the door of the Attaché's office, turned the knob, and let himself in. The Attaché's pert little secretary was at her desk, typing with a fury that was her trademark. Every bachelor in the Embassy had his eye on her as had half the married men.

17

"Hi," Stockton said grinning. "Where's Williams?"

She stopped her typing and answered, "He left about thirty minutes ago with Commander Smith-Hutton. How are you today, Mr. Stockton?"

Stockton realized he had been abrupt. He offered an apologetic smile and said, "Hi, again. I'm okay. Just a little wound-up."

She adjusted her skirt as she turned her chair slightly, then said, "It's getting that way, isn't it?"

Impatience nagged at him, but he checked himself. This girl was one of the few people on the Embassy staff who was civil to him.

"I guess so," he said abstractedly, then, veiling his impatience as much as possible, he asked, "Do you know where Lieutenant Gruenwald is?"

She paused for an instant and Stockton had the decided impression she was toying with the idea of not telling him the truth.

"Hey," he chided, "Come on. I've got to see him."

She weakened, grinned, then pressed the intercom button on her desk. She said into the machine, "Mr. Onett, Mr. Stockton is here to see Lieutenant Gruenwald."

The secretary gave him a bright wink as she waited for the reply. It was obvious that she had let some cat out of the bag and he was glad he had been careful to cultivate her. He could imagine Joe Onett, the Assistant Commercial Attaché, squirming in his office with Lieutenant Gruenwald, trying to decide how to avoid meeting with this unwanted visitor from State.

The Assistant Commercial Attaché's voice

came back, loaded with resignation: "Thanks a lot. Please send him in."

Stockton shot a wink of thanks to the girl as he crossed the reception room and let himself into Onett's office.

The room, like all of the working offices in the Embassy, was spartan: a medium-size desk, four chairs, a small bookcase, and an oscillating GE fan trying to stir up some air. Even the view out the window was austere, looking onto the parking area in the back of the compound. Some effort was required to see the well-manicured garden over by the high wall about a hundred feet away. Onett was on the telephone.

Stockton nodded to the two men in the room and said, "He's on the golf course by now. You'll have to do battle alone."

Ambassador Grew's nearly unbreakable schedule of golfing at the Tokyo Country Club was well known. The Ambassador contended that Mondays were virtually nonwork days, thanks to the fourteen-hour time difference and the International Date Line jump, it was Sunday in Washington and nothing ever happened in Washington on Sunday.

Placing his hand over the receiver, Joe Onett said, "I'm not trying to get him. Just have a seat."

Stockton pulled up a chair next to Lieutenant Gruenwald and said quietly, "You've got some excitement, I hear."

The young Naval officer shrugged his shoulders.

Onett dropped the telephone noisily back into its cradle. "Goddamned phones never work right," he grunted.

19

Ben tried to lighten the mood. "Just some of the joys of living in the Orient. What's up?"

Onett eased himself back in his swivel chair, plopped his feet up on an open drawer, and said with sarcasm, "You really do use finesse, Stockton."

"Look," Ben shot back, "I don't feel like getting into a farting contest with you, Onett. What's up?"

Everyone on the regular Embassy staff knew that, in spite of his apparently lowly position, Stockton was in Tokyo with plenipotentiary authority; that was why they shunned him, tried to keep him at bay. Ambassador Grew was quick to jump on anyone who recognized Ben's authority; such heresy had no place in the Great Joe Grew's regime. Grew had been the self-proclaimed god in the American Embassy in Tokyo for over nine years and his domain was to remain inviolate.

Both the Assistant Commercial Attaché and the Assistant Naval Attaché knew that Stockton moved in high circles. They would just as soon buck this interloper up in the chain of command, but they had to respond to his questions because their section chiefs were unavailable and would not be back for several hours.

The Navy lieutenant glanced pensively at Onett, then said, "Okay, Stockton. Here's what we've got."

The call had come in slightly after six that morning. On the surface, it seemed a routine, crank annoyance. The Office of Naval Intelligence had an agent out in the field, working under a civilian cover. His liaison pipeline was the Commercial Section of the Embassy. He had been scheduled to meet with one of his sources and report by telephone to Onett at his home by seven

20

o'clock. The agent was an exceptionally competent and reliable one and had never missed a pass-through appointment. Tying that to the threatening tone of the crank telephone call, the assumption had to be that something of a major nature had gone wrong. In addition, the call had come in on an unpublished, unlisted number used by ONI. A quick, urgent check was made on the intelligence contact and she had turned up dead.

Onett went on, "It was murder. Our source in Kyoto said she had been garotted. So . . . ."

Ben picked up the thought. "So either he killed her, or the Kempei did it."

"Right," the Navy lieutenant said. "Either way, he would have made contact with us. . . ."

Stockton cut in again. "Unless he's been taken . . . ."

"Or killed himself," said Onett.

The atmosphere in the office took on the aura of a wake as the three faced the probable realities of the situation.

After an extended pause, Stockton asked Lieutenant Gruenwald, "Can you fill me in? I know it might be too highly classified . . . ."

The Navy officer waved his hand in irritation at the situation. "What the hell difference can it make now?"

He spent a couple of minutes outlining the undercover operation and finished by observing that the agent was one of the most reliable men the Navy had in the field.

"What's Smith-Hutton up to?" Stockton asked.

Onett came into the conversation. "He's going down to Kobe with Frank Williams. Navy was using us for a cover so all the probing will have to be done by our Commercial office. We've got to know; but I hate to think what we're going to find out."

Impulsively Stockton asked, "Isn't this big enough for the Old Man to sacrifice his golf game?"

Onett bristled. "You'd better watch your protocol, Stockton; this is a pretty tight little Embassy."

Stockton did not respond; he had orders to work amiably with Ambassador Grew, but he did not see any reason for bootlicking. "Are you going to tell him?" he asked.

Onett replied bruskly, "When I'm told to."

Stockton was in no position to intervene; Onett was right in waiting for instructions from the Commercial Attaché, Frank Williams. Ambassador Grew's feisty way of handling subordinates was enough to justify Onett's position.

It would probably be three or four hours before the attachés would reach Kobe, so nothing more would be gained from that quarter for a little while; Ben took his leave.

The morning was already beginning to swelter and the hot sun made Stockton perspire as he crossed the parking area toward the dormitory building inside the Embassy compound where he had a room. As he reached the arched entrance, Ned Crocker, the First Secretary at the Embassy, was coming out.

"Hi, Stockton. I was looking for you."

"Crocker. What's up?"

"Mack wants to see you. Says it's important."

Stockton thought maybe the word on the Roosevelt-Churchill meeting had been passed down, but it was too early for such an announcement. He nodded to Crocker and indicated he'd come along. As they walked across the concrete

22

surface back toward the main building, Crocker asked, "How long are you going to be here?"

"Not long," Stockton replied. "Probably just a few days."

"But," Crocker came back, "Dooman won't be back for a couple of weeks."

Ben nodded agreement but did not reply; the Embassy's Counselor had nothing to do with his presence.

The Marine guard opened the door for them and they entered the building. Activity on the ground floor was beginning to pick up as the business day started. On their way up to Mack Priest's office on the second floor, they were greeted by polite morning salutations from various staff members.

Crocker and Stockton walked into Priest's office and were greeted with the familiar scowl. "Thanks, Crocker. Would you be a sport and go to the Code Room and pick up any new telegrams." His intention was obvious: Priest wanted Crocker out of the way.

Without invitation, Stockton sat down across the desk from Priest. As Crocker closed the door, Priest intoned in a pompous voice, "We need you to go up to Hokkaido. Probably for three or four days. You'll leave on the noon train for Aomori."

Ben made no overt reaction. He had no intention of going any place in Japan, let alone to an isolated island far to the north.

"It's a minor matter. It seems some of our people up there have been snagged with tummy trots and we need a man on the scene to insure proper medical attention."

Now Stockton knew they were trying to shunt him away—no one from the Embassy would be sent on such a minor mission. He pulled out a package of Chesterfields and lit one.

"Look, Stockton, I expect some respect from you. Now I've told you what's expected. You get moving."

Ben leaned forward and said quietly, "I'm not going any place, Mack. So don't waste our time."

Priest was furious. "You'd better learn your place, Stockton," he shouted. "You're getting. . . ."

Ben cut him off. "I know my place, Mack. You're not the man who can tell me what to do."

Mack Priest, an educated Arkansas hillbilly, was a protégé of Ambassador Grew. Because his personal background offered little in the way of qualifications—family, schooling, or experience— he was insecure whenever he was challenged. Stockton knew this so he did not press the advantage; he simply refused to acknowledge any authority on Priest's part.

Mack pushed his stocky frame up out of the chair, dropping his gold-rimmed glasses in the process. Fumbling to put them back in place, he said, "This is an instruction from the Ambassador. Who do you think you are, challenging his authority?"

Calmly, Ben asked, "Is he in?"

Flustered by Stockton's casualness, Priest did not reply. He only stood there, glaring.

Ben said, "The Ambassador, I mean. Is he in? I'd like to see him."

Unable to comprehend such insubordination, Priest stood there, working himself into a new rage. Finally, with great effort, he said, "The Ambassador is not in the compound. He has ordered that you get the noon train. You'd better be on it."

Ben snuffed out his cigarette in an ash tray,

stood up, and said, "I'll go see him." He turned and walked away.

Priest yelled after him as Stockton pulled the door shut. "You lousy sonovabitch," he was shouting. "You better be on that train."

As he walked down the hall, Stockton could hear crude curses following him from Priest's office. Mack was not known for finesse or delicacy.

Down in the entrance foyer, he requested a car to be brought around.

CHAPTER 3

TOKYO, JAPAN

AUGUST 11, 1941

The barmen were furiously busy polishing glasses at the far end of the room, and a young man wearing the purple and white uniform of the Tokyo Country Club was standing on a chair cleaning the tall windows as Stockton talked quietly with Ambassador Joseph Grew.

"I know, sir," Stockton replied with the necessary note of contrition on his voice.

"Then," Grew said pompously, "never, young man, never act so presumptuous again. I'll not have my juniors barging into areas where they do not belong."

Ben stifled an urge to blast the Ambassador's arrogance. Instead, he said quietly, "I apologize, sir, but I felt you were ill-advised in selecting me for the assignment in Hokkaido; I must be on duty at the Embassy for the next several days."

Grew knitted his bushy eyebrows. "I'm not privy to your importance in my mission, Mr. Stockton. Possibly you might care to enlighten me?"

Stockton's orders from State in Washington called for him to observe and report the Japanese reaction to the Churchill-Roosevelt meeting, and he had been specifically instructed not to reveal anything about the meeting; an untainted reaction report was considered important.

Embarrassed, but tempted to tell Grew it was none of his business, Stockton summoned up some diplomatic tact. "I'm sorry, sir, but we all have our orders. With all due respect, we will be able to discuss it in a few days, I'm sure."

Grew puffed little spurts of air out through his lightly pressed lips; Ben was distracted by the tufts of mustache hair flitting back and forth.

"Sir," Ben jumped impatiently ahead, "Could I beg your permission for something I feel is critical to my assignment?"

Grew's hands flew up in a display of exaggerated impatience. He hissed out, "My God, man, what has possessed you to recognize that I have any authority here in my own Embassy?"

Stockton smiled, hoping the Ambassador's sarcasm might indicate a waning hostility. "I am," he said, "in a rather embarrassing...."

But Grew continued speaking. "You come out here and interrupt me. You seem oblivious of the fact that General Ott has a starting time just ten minutes behind us. Do you have any idea how much effort was invested in getting out onto the course before General Ott?"

Stockton's face registered blank incomprehension.

Grew's eyes opened wide as he nodded angrily, "No. I'm sure you don't give a tinker's damn about such things."

Grew's voice rose slightly. Stockton noticed that one of the dining room waiters had moved closer to them, trying to appear busy wiping down a spotless table top.

"You are obviously not attuned to the delicate situation here, Stockton," Grew said. Ben nodded slightly toward the suspicious waiter, but Grew shrugged aside the warning. Having spent nine years in Japan, he had studiously avoided learning the language, and he seemed to think that if he could not understand the locals, they could not understand him.

"I think," Grew offered, "We'd better make some arrangements for you to return to the States."

Grew was partially deaf so Stockton could not lower his voice too much or he would not be heard at all. "Could we go outside, sir?" he asked.

Impatient to end the annoying meeting, Grew led the way out of the lounge to the wide patio. They walked over to the far side where they could see Grew's golfing companions waiting at the first tee.

"I want to go and see Schreiber," Stockton said abruptly.

The statement stunned Grew so much that he actually took a step backward. Ricardo Rivera Schreiber was the ranking member of the Peruvian mission in Tokyo. He held the rank of Minister. For Ben Stockton, a very junior officer attached to the American Embassy, to make such a suggestion was far beyond Grew's comprehension.

"You seem, sir," Grew said in a loud voice, "to have lost any perspective you may have once had. Your request cannot be granted; it is unthinkable. I fear I must take steps to remove you from my staff, Stockton. You are not only a dangerous thinking person, but you seem to lack any idea of what is done within the Foreign Service. I will telegraph the Secretary today and have you recalled. I do not give a hoot what your assignment is; I'll not have you destroying all I have worked for over these many years."

Stockton looked around to make sure they would not be overheard. "I want to see Schreiber because of the Pearl Harbor thing," he said. Grew nodded impatient understanding. "I'm sure you've heard about the conference at the Imperial Navy College?" Grew nodded again and Ben continued. "And the ONI man who turned up missing last night?" There was another aggravated nod from the Ambassador. "Well, sir, I think they might be tied together. I have a very strong feeling. . . ."

Grew raised his hand with an emphatic gesture that would have done a traffic cop credit. Anger accented his words. "Young man, I've heard enough. The Peruvian Minister is a gentle and concerned man, and any liaison with him will be handled by me and only me. Is that clear?" Grew did not wait for an answer. "The Naval Conference is the business of the Imperial Government and is not to be the object of casual speculation on your part. When the time comes, I will compile a despatch for the Secretary, but that will come only after careful and well-studied analysis. As far as the 'missing'—as you term it—American in Kyoto, if he is missing, then that will come to us through the proper channels, and if he was an

ONI agent, then he knew the risks of meddling in a country that is trying very hard to get along with us in extremely difficult times."

Grew paused and Stockton jumped in. "There are strong rumors that the Navy meeting is being held to discuss the possibility of an attack on Pearl Harbor. It is possible—even probable—that the ONI man was on to that intelligence."

Grew let out a sigh of obvious impatience. "Stockton, you have a lot to learn. For your information, there are always rumors flitting about Tokyo about an attack on Pearl Harbor. I reported just that months ago."

"Yes, sir," Stockton agreed, "and you said that the rumor had no substance."

"Which was true," Grew retorted angrily. "This city is rampant with rumors of attacks on Pearl Harbor, of attacks on Singapore or Hong Kong, of attacks on the Philippines. Hell, Stockton, if I ran this Embassy on rumors of attacks, I'd have no time for the vital job of ensuring peace. There is a faction in this country that would be delighted to have us think such a thing. But the important forces in Japan, the real leaders of this empire, are not only against war, they are working valiantly to build a peace for all of the Pacific and Asia."

Stockton thought of Japan's long, protracted invasion of China and the recent moves the Japanese had made into Indo-China, but he kept quiet, hoping to clear his proposed meeting with the Peruvian Minister.

"I am in close touch with the highest levels of the Japanese government," Grew continued, "and, believe me, they are more anxious than we are to avoid conflict and promote peace. Good God, man, I talk with them regularly and I'd know if something was afoot. I do not intend to let them even think that we are concerned with aggression on their part. It is the furthest thing from their minds; I can guarantee that after my years and years of experience with them."

"I certainly do not challenge your experience, Mr. Ambassador. I merely want to talk with Schreiber. What harm can it do?"

Suddenly, Grew's entire body stiffened, then convulsed and, for a second, Stockton thought the Ambassador might be suffering some kind of stroke. Then, in a stage gesture, Grew's arm flew forward and pointed out toward the entrance driveway of the club. Ben looked and saw the long, dark gray Mercedes-Benz limousine speeding up the graveled road. General Ott, the German Ambassador to Japan, was arriving for his golf date.

"See what you've done," Grew whined. "Do you understand the mess you have caused?"

Not trying to hide the disgust in his voice, Stockton said, "I'll leave. May I see the Minister?"

His voice trembling, Grew began to move toward the stairs and path that would hurry him to the first tee. "You stay away from him," he called back. "That is an order. Stay away."

Ben Stockton stood there for a couple of minutes, watching Grew stride onto the course. Out on the first tee the British Ambassador, Sir Robert Craigie, was placing his ball. Grew received a friendly wave from Craigie's partner and Shiro Akaboshi, the club's golf pro who made up the foursome. Grew teed up next and—either out of anger or bad habit—took an overly strong swing. The ball hooked nastily, and Stockton was

sure Grew would lay that one down to him and
his distracting plans.

"Shit," Ben thought to himself, "If I'm going
to be accused of that sin, I might as well go all
the way."

He walked back through the club, nodded politely to the entourage surrounding General Ott,
and went out to his car. He told the driver:
"Take me to the Peruvian Legation."

As the car circled out the driveway, Stockton
looked off to the right and watched the foursome
hurrying down the first fairway. They were chatting happily and he wondered how Grew, with all
the turmoil in the world and with the obvious
dangers to his own country, could be displaying
such a nonchalant attitude toward his country's
peril. But then he remembered what had happened several months before, when Grew was
first exposed to the Pearl Harbor report.

CHAPTER 4

TOKYO, JAPAN

JANUARY 27, 1941

The soft chamber music was somehow incongru-
ous, out of place. Several couples danced in a manner that suggested they would just as soon be at
home, or at the movies, or any place rather than
where they were—in the residence of the American Embassy in Tokyo.

But, in the penumbral social aspects of diplomatic life, people had to attend and perform according to a rigid code of behavior. A Commercial Attaché from a "neutral country"—say Börg Kristensen of the Swedish Embassy—would virtually use a stopwatch to divide seconds equally between innocuous chatter with Lt. Wilton Persman, ADC to British Ambassador Sir Robert Craigie, and superficial discussions with Herr Gunther Werner, Transportation Advisor to German Ambassador Count Eugen Ott.

During the delicately timed arrivals and departures of belligerent nations' Ambassadors and their particular entourages, safe ports of refuge could be found among clusters of insignificant nonbelligerent personnel from uncommitted countries such as Switzerland, Portugal, Sweden. It was in these islands of safe territory that protocol permitted knocking back a quick drink in an attempt to reduce tension.

Just after 8:40 that night, during the lull created between the departure of the British delegation and the arrival of the German contingent, Ned Crocker, First Secretary of the U.S. Embassy in Tokyo, eased up to his Ambassador Joseph Grew and began a casual chat, a signal that he wanted to talk privately with the Ambassador. Such conversations during that period in pre-war Japan were extremely limited. One could talk about Jimmy Demaret winning the Masters, but surely any comparison to Richard Burton's victory in the British Open was in poor taste. Joe Louis' knockout of Al McCoy six weeks before was a bit touchy even though it had been two and a half years since the Brown Bomber had decked Max Schmeling. Crocker's innocent conversation was about flowers; a totally acceptable subject in

32

a country where the Emperor was an avid nature lover. Grew and Crocker exchanged unimportant words as they deftly jockeyed into a vacant space in the reception hall where there was some insulation from listening ears in the middle of the crowded room.

"We've got another rumor-monger working tonight," Crocker announced quietly.

Grew preened his mustache as he said, "What is it?"

"The wild word is that our host country is planning," Crocker lowered his voice even more as he continued, "planning to bomb Pearl Harbor."

Thirty years in the Foreign Service had prepared Ambassador Grew to display a stoic expression. His personal belief that the Japanese sheltered no ill feelings toward the United States prompted a reply which telegraphed his contempt for such an idea: "We would want to quash any stories which are not sound in their basis."

"We have the source pocketed in the lounge," Crocker whispered. "Dooman is with him." Eugene Dooman was one of Grew's closest advisors.

"Who?"

"Valdez. Peruvian Legation."

"Documented?"

"Oral," Crocker replied.

Grew paused in contemplation. He glanced over at the flurry of activity at the entrance foyer which indicated the arrival of the German delegation. Quickly, Grew demanded, "Does he know what he is talking about?"

"I think he is speaking for Schreiber," Crocker replied.

As host, Grew was anxious to assume his place in the reception line; he was a man who placed diplomatic protocol above all else in life. As he moved away from Crocker, he said in a hushed tone, "This can wait until tomorrow. Get me some facts."

Ned Crocker did not presume to answer or to try to press his point. Proper form in the State Department back in that decade did not allow for challenge. He turned and, with a moderate display of haste, headed for the secluded, private lounge at the rear of the residency.

While most eyes in the room were beginning to lock on the arriving German Ambassador and his group, Kiyoshi Hirazawa, a seemingly low-level official in the American Bureau of the Imperial Foreign Office, noticed Eugene Dooman's departure, and he quickly began a visual inventory of those present in the reception hall. A total of two and a half minutes were required for Hirazawa's facile brain to note that the Peruvian, José Valdez, was not accounted for. He whispered to his wife, Toshiko, to avail herself of the powder room facilities back near the lounge and report back to him everything she was able to see, especially if she saw Crocker talking with Valdez.

In the quiet of the lounge, one could almost sense José Valdez's heart beating in excitement, even over his quiet protest. "I've got to get back in there. My absence will be noticed." Crocker had come into the room and delivered Grew's message to Dooman and Valdez. Eugene Dooman looked at the Peruvian with contempt. Dooman was an old Japan hand. He had been born in Osaka and consequently was a BIJ—Born in Japan—American diplomat and, because he spoke Japanese fluently, he had little regard for Latin accents, which led in part to his contempt for Valdez. Mostly, Dooman did not like what Valdez

34

was saying because it contradicted his own and the Ambassador's positive opinion that the problems existing between Japan and the United States were going to be resolved peacefully, that there would be no war.

"Why," Dooman asked Valdez, "do you insist that this information—this *rumor*—is authentic?"

Valdez was getting more and more impatient. He was angry with himself for offering the message to Dooman at all. "I am speaking for my Minister," Valdez retorted with an edge of anger beginning to show in his voice.

"Really," Dooman came back with a condescending tone which showed little respect. "Why didn't your Minister tell us directly?"

Valdez had not been the man to send as a competent messenger. He did not know the rules of the game and he did not know the strength he had as a spokesman for his legation. He meekly replied, "I will ask my chief that question for you."

Dooman offered a superficial smile of friendship as he made a shallow attempt to butter up Valdez. "Now, that will not be necessary. Why don't you ask your Minister to come and talk with me? We can get at the root of this right now."

Valdez was aware of the basics of protocol. "That is impossible and you know it," he answered.

Indeed, Dooman did know this would violate protocol, but it amused him to explore the lengths to which he could push the hopeless Latin. "Why not have your Minister pay us a visit tomorrow," he suggested. "Then we can let the two chiefs have a nice discussion."

Valdez's Latin temper began flaring and, in spite of his hushed tones, his anger was evident. "That's what I asked you in the *first* place. 'Will Ambassador Grew be interested in hearing about a proposed plan to bomb Pearl Harbor?' That's what I asked you."

Dooman took a moment to light a cigarette before he replied, "I was just trying to save Ambassador Grew time; I'm sure you can understand."

The insulting implications of his comment managed to slip past Valdez who now insisted, "I must return. I have been gone too long. May my Minister come tomorrow at ten?"

Dooman merely nodded his acceptance of the time, then he moved toward the door and said, "Let me see that the coast is clear."

Dooman was looking back over his shoulder as he eased the door open, so he did not notice that Toshiko Hirazawa had had her body tilted slightly inward toward the door in a vain attempt to hear what was being said. She made a meek gesture of embarrassment and explained in broken English that she had been looking for the powder room. In perfect and gentle Japanese, Dooman said, "Oh, my dear. It is down the hall on the other side."

She came back in her confident native tongue. "I see. Thank you. I'm very sorry." And she turned quickly, scurrying off to complete her unnecessary trip to the powder room.

Dooman pulled the door open and looked toward the other end of the hall; it was clear. He turned to Valdez and asked, "How'd you like to take a shot at that little Japanese piece?"

There was a discernible quiver in Valdez's voice. "She saw me. She's Hirazawa's wife."

Dooman shook his head. "No she didn't. She

was probably trying to see if I was alone. I must say I wouldn't mind laying my leg over that little. . . ."

Valdez cut him off with, "I must return to the hall. I've been gone too long."

Dooman stepped back and said, "Have a good evening. We'll be expecting your Minister at ten tomorrow morning."

Back in the reception hall, the German delegation had arrived, been received, and was well dispersed throughout the crowd, performing their customary ritual. Normally, cryptology people were not part of a visiting contingent, but on this particular evening, Lt. Col. Heinz Baum was along and not to enjoy the gaiety of the party. Baum, resident ABWEHR agent of the *Fremde Heere Ost* and responsible for various evaluation duties in the East, was looking for a crypto he knew would be attending. Cryptologists frequently come out of their mysterious caves to drift among diplomatic gatherings in hopes of overhearing one of those tricky code names which begin popping up in top secret messages. A really good crypto can do wonders with a word if he can find out who is using it and where it is being bantered about. ("Overlord," code name for the invasion of Normandy was, in fact, blown when it was dropped accidently within earshot of a Turkish diplomat; only Hitler's whim prevented that slip from causing a disaster.)

Lieutenant Colonel Baum spotted his target: Kiyoshi Hirazawa. By the time Hirazawa's petite wife had joined them, Kiyoshi had lost all interest in the missing Peruvian diplomat, Valdez. Baum had brought intelligence that the Americans had been able to break the B-machine, Japan's ultimate code device which, until that moment, had been considered unbreakable and vital to Japanese plans for their Greater East Asia Co-Prosperity Sphere. Twice in the next five minutes, Kiyoshi's wife tried to mention seeing Valdez with Dooman, but to no avail. Within a few minutes more, Kiyoshi left the reception alone, instructed an assistant to see that his wife was taken home, and then hastily departed for his office in the Foreign Office. His wife managed to forget all about her assignment because her husband's preoccupation with the code machine problem seemed to be the most important thing in the world.

Next morning, Minister Ricardo Rivera Schreiber, representing the Republic of Peru, managed to visit the U.S. Embassy and deliver a piece of his own intelligence to Ambassador Joseph Grew. He was offering the United States a ten-month running start to make preparations for countering, defeating, or even, perhaps, preventing a sneak attack on military and naval installations on the island of Hawaii.

"A fascinating piece of gossip, Ricardo," Grew said as he tilted his body forward and lifted the delicate porcelain pot. "More coffee?" The Peruvian Minister nodded politely. "You know," Grew went on as he poured, "this profession of ours is changing daily." Another patient nod.

"Time was," Grew continued, "when only gentlemen were allowed into our fraternity. But over the past few years, changes have been encouraged from sources which would destroy the very fiber of the Foreign Service. I'm sure you have felt the same pressures from your government in Lima?"

"I don't know what you mean, Señor," the visitor said with sincerity.

Grew settled back onto the couch and primped his mustache before drinking his coffee. "I mean," Grew explained, "some of these people we have to accept in the attaché area. Really gauche types who are nothing more than spies; men not really suited for the fragile life of diplomacy."

"Your point, Señor?" the Peruvian asked with some impatience.

"Please," Grew offered with a broad smile, "please do understand me. My point is that people here within my own Embassy are frequently trying to slip out of their proper duties."

There was a slightly louder noise than necessary as Schreiber placed the cup and saucer down on the marble coffee table. "I hope you did not intend to offend me, Señor Grew. I am merely relaying to you what I have heard. I am taking great risks in even mentioning this to you."

"My dear friend," Grew solicited, "the last thing I want is to offend you. I accept your information with great thanks. But I am beginning to weary of the constant rumors."

Grew rose and began walking about the room so that the Peruvian had a hard time following his travels. "I've had immense problems. A couple of months ago one of my juniors obtained complete working drawings of the Imperial Army's type 99 machine gun. Now that is just not the sort of thing that is to go in our pouches, I mean, after all. . . ."

The visitor gave up craning his neck and he stared down at the half-empty coffee cup. Grew was at the window and continued, "A couple of years ago I had a terrible time with one of my men—Schuler. Frank Schuler, did you ever meet him?"

"I can't remember."

"Not all that important. What was silly was he constantly managed to meddle in very sticky areas. This Schuler would make trips out into the countryside in order to check certain roads. He was proud as a cock-rooster when he located a military highway that was listed as a dirt road."

The Peruvian noted, "He seems to have taken some initiative. . . ."

Grew pranced back across the room and sat down again as he countered, "Sure, he took an initiative. He found a simple error on the map and discovered a four-lane highway with military convoys moving on it. He also got himself interrogated by the military police and could have caused incredible turmoil. I mean, really; it is not the job of my Third Secretaries to go snooping around and playing modern day Mata Hari's. Fortunately, he got himself mixed up in a romance that went sour and he asked to be transferred home. Just as well, too. I don't need people like that on my team."

The Peruvian Minister stood up. He said with a noticeable degree of coolness, "I see now that I have made a grave error in bothering you with this. I hope you will forgive me."

"Now, now, now," Grew protested, gesturing for the man to resume his seat. As the visitor settled back down, Grew said, "You misunderstand me, Schreiber. I appreciate your report. I promise that I will send it along this very day. I will send a telegram and follow it up with a despatch in the next pouch. Believe me, I do appreciate your report." Grew paused, felt a sense of placidity come over his face, then said, "But I do so much like to send more encouraging news home. I am always pleased when I have a good meeting with Prince Konoye; he is such a decent chap."

Schreiber nodded, "I find the Prime Minister a good politician."

"He is our man," Grew said with obvious glee. "He will make this whole thing work out well. I have never felt closer to any Prime Minister than I feel to the Prince. I feel we will see a solid peace in the near future."

"With all due respect, Señor Grew," the Peruvian said, "I think you place too much value on the Prince. He is just as bad as the others."

A smug grin appeared on Grew's face. "When you have been here as long as I have, dear Schreiber, you will think differently." Grew had arrived in 1932; Schreiber in 1938, but the Peruvian did not acknowledge longevity as any measure of particular competence. He replied, "I hope we will all see a long service here, but, realistically, I cannot see much of a future. Not with them planning to bomb your country and demolish your Navy."

Grew raised a finger in a mock-scolding manner. "Now, you are succumbing to your rumors. Let's give them a chance."

"I hope you have the chance," Schreiber replied.

Grew looked at his watch. "I really must tear myself away now, dear friend." He stood and reached to take his guest's arm. "Now you rest assured that I will send off a telegram today. I will send a despatch later and mention your name specifically. It would be unwise to put your name in the cable; security and all of that, you know."

"I know, all too well. Do you want to know my source's name?"

Grew shook his head. "Now that would be out

41

of place, wouldn't it? No, that is not proper or necessary. Surely your word alone will carry a heavy weight when it gets to the Secretary in Washington."

As they walked into the reception area, Grew said, "Do, let's stay in close touch. I know we are both busy, but we both have our duties and you are doing yours better than anyone in the whole Tokyo diplomatic corps."

Schreiber was buoyed by the flattery, especially because some of Grew's staff were waiting impatiently for the meeting to end and Grew's compliments were overheard by all in the reception room.

As soon as the Peruvian Minister was properly escorted to his auto, Dooman joined Grew in the Ambassador's office.

"Was it anything?" Dooman asked.

Grew slid into the chair behind his large desk and replied, "A bunch of clap-trap. I swear I don't know what some nations think of . . . sending a man like that to such a high post. Simple, dangerous rumor-mongering. We'd better send it along in a cable, then file a despatch. But I want it clear that we put little or no credence in such gossip. You compose the working, then let me see it."

Dooman nodded, then said, "Count Kabayama wants you to have lunch at the Kaigun Club."

Grew beamed. The president of Nippon Steel having lunch at the exclusive Navy Club was important. "Now that, Dooman, is the kind of meeting to have. Our Latin friend might like to gossip, but Kabayama is a man of substance. Is my schedule free?"

Dooman nodded and said, "I accepted for you."

Grew smiled, "Good man."

CHAPTER 5

TOKYO, JAPAN

AUGUST 11, 1941

"Thank you for seeing me, Your Excellency," Stockton said as he tried to settle back comfortably in the overstuffed chair.

The Peruvian Minister's office was adequate for its purposes, but it was startlingly different from Ambassador Grew's elegant setting. Schreiber had expended only limited funds for décor. The furniture was all Japanese made; only the wall decorations seemed to be from Peru and those were obviously there courtesy of the Moore-Mac Lines; each had a modest tag that encouraged: Visit Peru.

"I am curious as to how I can be of aid to you, Señor Stockton."

Ben forced a smile and swallowed hard; he was really leaving himself open for a blast from Ambassador Grew.

"I had better tell you right away, sir, that I am here on my own initiative. I asked Ambassador Grew's permission to see you, but he refused. I felt it was imperative that I speak to you."

"It must have been very imperative, Señor Stockton," Schreiber replied. "You put me in an awkward position by telling me this."

Ben used every mental resource he had available to convey his good intentions. For a quarter of an hour the two men discussed career obligations and responsibilities in the Foreign Service. Ben bared his own feelings as clearly as he possibly could.

"I'm convinced," Schreiber told the American, "that this will be only between you and me. Now, what can I do for you?"

Stockton felt a wave of relief. "Back in January," he began, "you heard something about a sneak attack on Pearl Harbor, and you reported it to our people."

A broad, toothy grin came to the Peruvian's face. "So," he said with a pleased tone, "the old 'fairy tale' has surfaced again. You know, don't you, that Ambassador Grew actually called my warning a 'fairy tale'? Did you know that?"

Ben shook his head. "No, sir."

"Well, he did. And I have let it lie there. I have no reason to impose such 'fairy tales' on your government."

"Could you go back, sir. Could you go back in your mind and tell me the information again?"

Schreiber hesitated. He had been offended by Ambassador Grew's arrogance and he did not care to expose himself to yet another indignity. But this time Stockton had come to him and he seemed to be sincere.

Schreiber, for several months, had had his own reservations about the intelligence. Back in January, when he had relayed the tip to Grew, he had been under the impression that the attack on Pearl Harbor was imminent. When the attack did not take place, he had wondered about the truth of the story. But recent developments had explained the time lag. New information he had received put the previous tip in better perspective. Neverthe-

44

less, he had decided to avoid the possibility of an insult from Grew by remaining silent. Functioning in his primary capacity, he had relayed the new intelligence to his own government in Peru and included a suggestion that it be relayed to Washington. But Schreiber would not approach Grew again. Now, with Ben Stockton facing him, Schreiber had a new decision to make. After consideration, he decided to talk.

"You must realize that there is a certain jeopardy to third parties in this, Señor Stockton. Not only must you be discreet about how you handle this information, you must also guard even your thoughts so that you do not reveal what you know."

Stockton nodded his understanding.

"The report," the Minister explained, "came to me from a very unlikely source. I have a valet, a likeable, friendly man who has been with our legation for several years. He has had some minor family problems which are not related to this incident, but I helped him over some rough times. We have established a close, personal relationship. By one of those quirks of fate—do you believe in fate, Señor Stockton?" Ben nodded. "Well, by one of those quirks of fate, my valet's brother is in the Imperial Navy. He is not a high-ranking officer or anything like that. He is only a middle-level clerk. But, in the ways of the world, the powerful leaders and dynamic planners must, at some time, rely on middle-level clerks. Such are the whims of history."

Ben squirmed impatiently. He fought back an impulse to try to hurry Schreiber along, but he knew the Latin personality well enough to check his urge.

"As fate would have it," Schreiber continued,

45

"the family got together one night and, in the normal course of things, sake was consumed. I think it was around the feast of Ebisu Matsuri and the family spirits were high. So were the alcohol spirits." Schreiber smiled at his little joke and Ben managed a broad grin of appreciation. The Minister went on, "The talk got around to world tensions and my valet mentioned the broad American financial involvement in Peru. This was in conjunction with something about the natural resources of the United States; my man was pointing out that the U.S. could also depend on other nation's resources, such as Peru's. His brother took issue with this, pointing out that resources were not the ultimate strength of a nation, that national will was also a vital factor. The brother bragged that Japan's will, the dedication to the Imperial purpose could surmount an advantage in natural resources. My valet raised the point that the Americans seemed to have, when necessary, a strong will. As a counter to this, the brother in the Imperial Navy suggested that possibly the will of the Americans might be easily broken. The discussion went on for quite a while before it came out that the War Plans Division of the Imperial Navy was working on a secret, massive attack on Pearl Harbor. This was not a slight piece of bragging; he mentioned the type of attack it would be, the objectives of the attack, and even the creator of the attack plan, Admiral Yamamoto."

Stockton raised his hand in protest and said, "But none of these things showed up in Ambassador Grew's telegram. He merely mentioned the rumor."

Schreiber nodded. "That would be quite right.

46

He seemed to ignore the details; he did not want to hear any of it when I met with him."

"Why?"

"Who knows," the Minister said with resignation. "I was told that it would be out of place for him to inquire. I had the feeling that we were playing a game of traditionally structured diplomatic politics. We must play by the rules, Old Chap' sort of thing. That is the only justification I can offer for Grew's attitude. Why not check with him?"

"In case you haven't guessed, Mr. Minister," Stockton said lightly, "I'm not in the best of graces with the Ambassador. I am not here permanently, just on a special assignment."

Politely, Schreiber asked, "To do with the Pearl Harbor warning?"

"No, sir. Another matter. But I have an interest in your warning. I read the telegram and despatch that were sent. They have not had the impact they should have in Washington. But then there was no reason for anyone to react strongly."

Schreiber frowned. "What do you mean by that?" he asked. "What could be said that could cause more concern?"

"Well, sir," Stockton explained, "I read the despatch personally. It clearly said: 'The Embassy places no credence in Schreiber's story.' I remember the words distinctly. So you see that it was not the sort of thing that would set off alarms all over the State Department."

The Peruvian's face grew red with anger. Sternly, he demanded, "Who would have said those words that way?"

Stockton stumbled as he explained, "It would

have been drafted by one of the people in the Embassy, maybe Dooman."

Schreiber came back, "But Grew would have known the wording?"

"Surely, it went over in his name."

"But, possibly," Schreiber groped, "it could have been paraphrased by one of your code clerks in Washington?"

Ben nodded. "On the telegram, it would surely have been paraphrased so that the actual words of the message would be different from what was relayed for distribution. That is a device we use so that the integrity of our code system can be maintained. But please understand, sir, I was referring to the despatch, the document that came over in the diplomatic pouch would be in clear language. There could be no loss of intent or meaning in a despatch. I simply assumed that the information was a casual story you had politely relayed to Ambassador Grew."

Schreiber leaned forward and used a pencil as a pointer for emphasis. "There was nothing casual, unless you consider the way the information was received by Grew. I was dead serious but obviously he did not take it seriously."

The two men sat there, digesting the new developments. Schreiber's pride was injured; Ben was trying to grasp the enormity of what he had heard. Both were faced with a real dilemma: The warning had been given urgently, yet nothing had happened. Pearl Harbor had not been attacked.

Stockton spoke first: "Maybe, sir, the tip was, in fact, only about a contingency plan. Maybe there was no real basis for fear." Then, feebly, he added, "Maybe Ambassador Grew was right in discounting the threat as having no credence."

Schreiber ran his hand through his thinning, blond hair and said in a calm voice, "I am not in Japan to play detective for your government, but I will tell you this : The story had credence. I will tell you one more thing and this you can handle as you wish. There are meetings going on right now at the Naval War College, right here in Tokyo, and one of the things they are discussing is the execution of the attack on Pearl Harbor."

That came as no shock or surprise to Stockton. The Embassy had gotten whiffs of rumors about the extraordinary meeting being attended by the major commanders in the Imperial Navy. Gossip coming out of the meeting had mentioned Pearl Harbor, but then it had also mentioned a dozen or more possible moves on the part of the fleet. The rumors were the basis for a lot of speculation, but no one was giving any hard analysis to them. Stockton remembered that Ned Crocker had told him about a staff meeting where he had brought up the subject and Dooman had exploded into a tirade about such conjectures; Ambassador Grew had nodded his head in agreement all through the blast. After that, the matter was taboo around the Embassy.

Stockton acknowledged the existence of the rumors.

Schreiber said, "Then you can do one thing for your country. You can get that word back and tell your government that they are in peril. It is none of my business, but Ambassador Grew seems to be functioning as if he had some special niche in destiny. I've seen him playing to the so-called anti-war element; there is no such element in Japan today. Grew has convinced himself that he can accomplish peace by promoting the pacifists here. Go look for yourself. There is only a facade of pacifism; this country wants war, any place, any time, with anyone who will come forward. Japan is going to spread out and get control of what it wants. If that means taking on the United States, then that will happen."

The silence in the room after Schreiber's diatribe was interrupted only by the quiet buzz of the overhead fan stirring up the hot afternoon air. Stockton did not know what to say. The Peruvian Minister had merely voiced an opinion; some ideas; a mass of conjecture. On the other side of the scale was the heavy weight in favor of Ambassador Grew's position. Grew had nearly ten years in service in Japan; he was well placed in social and diplomatic circles; his lengthy despatches were seemingly detailed and balanced. Maybe, because of passion or pride, some observers—like Schreiber—were not objective enough. Grew had frequently referred to the military presence in the government of Japan, forces that wanted war. But these despatches were always peppered with counterbalancing reports on the activities of the anti-war factions. Could Grew, with all of his experience and knowledge, be so wrong as to be completely, diametrically opposed to a man like Schreiber? If Schreiber was right, then Ambassador Grew was dead wrong. In the final analysis, Stockton had to feel that such a thing was not possible.

He had come to Schreiber and found only a tidbit, an explanation of the Pearl Harbor warning of the previous January. Other than that, he had merely added to apparently unfounded rumors about recent activities on the part of the Imperial Navy. None of the rumors could be solidly confirmed. Stockton would have to assume that Grew was reacting correctly to bits of unconfirmed information. Foreign policy could not be formulated on rumor. Stockton thanked the Peruvian Minister for his time and rose to take his leave.

As the two men shook hands, Schreiber asked, "Can you do anything with what I have told you?"

Stockton was inclined to be cautious. "I will certainly report it in the manner you gave it to me, sir."

"To Grew?"

Stockton smiled. "No, sir. I will report it in Washington. I am due to return shortly. I promise I will relay what you have told me. Thank you again."

CHAPTER 6

TOKYO, JAPAN

AUGUST 13, 1941

Lt. Comdr. Nakaya rehearsed the coming day of glory in his mind. He was daydreaming again. In his reverie, he banked his Mitsubishi A6M2-21 Zero steeply to the left and watched as a three-element formation of Aichi D3A1 "Val" dive bombers nosed down toward Ford Island. He could see the 551-pound bombs shackled between each Val's fixed landing gear and he could feel the excitement of the dive-bomber pilots as they plunged toward the moorings of Battleship Row on the east side of the island. Nakaya's Zero darted into a black, billowing cloud of oil smoke and his view was cut off for a couple of seconds. In that time, the Vals had released their bombs and were pulling up dramatically, turning hard to take up headings for Kaneohe Field back to the east. Suddenly, one of the three dive bombers cartwheeled grotesquely as a frightful black explosion erupted under one of its wings. An anti-aircraft shell had hit with either luck or remarkable precision, but no matter, the aircraft was lost. The two remaining planes clawed the air for more altitude on a heading for their target. Those two would each carry two 132-pound bombs to do their damage. With a silent prayer for the lost airmen, Nakaya steered for Walker Field to make one final check on the remainder of his Zeros which were strafing and probably nearly out of ammunition. Below him, the last of the three-man, Nakajima B5N2 "Kate" torpedo bombers were dropping their revolutionary new, shallow-running torpedos which had made the raid on Pearl Harbor possible. Earlier, he had watched the first waves of attackers plunge down on such behemoths as the U.S.S. *Arizona*, U.S.S. *Oklahoma* and U.S.S. *Nevada*. He had seen the aircraft carrier U.S.S. *Enterprise* burning and the cluster of destroyers near Pearl City ablaze. But the losses had been considerable; a calculated expenditure of men and equipment to deal a crushing blow. From what he had seen and the radio reports he had heard during the strike, he calculated a loss of forty-two aircraft and ninety-three airmen. It was sad to think of those sacrificed fliers, but the event itself was an outstanding triumph for the Imperial Navy. Off to his right, he could see Lieutenant Commander Shimazaki, leader of the second wave, coming up and flying off Nakaya's wing tip. They gave each other a victory sign, began climbing for altitude, and headed back toward the carrier *Kaga* that was waiting for them 230 miles to the north.

Suddenly, Lieutenant Commander Nakaya was snapped violently out of his cockpit, away from the roaring envelope of sound from his engine, and torn from his sweet taste of a glorious triumph.

Task Force Chief of Staff, Rear Admiral Matome Ugaki asked the question again: "Will you need the recovery submarines, Commander?"

Nakaya brought his eyes back into focus and looked around the room. The huge model of Oahu Island had come to life for him over the past few minutes and he had lost all touch with the dozen or so fellow officers who were talking about the attack.

Talking quietly to cover his embarrassment, Nakaya replied, "I think, sir, that we can make the landing decks if we once clear the strike area. Any crippled aircraft on the route back to the fleet would be very difficult to locate. My fliers will make it home."

Admiral Kinsu Kiyamoto, a crusty old submariner, spoke in a voice of gravel: "My transport submarines will be in the area as part of the launching operation. I challenge the Commander's ability to evaluate the skills of my crews in locating a downed aircraft."

Vice Admiral Chuichi Nagumo, who would be the attack fleet commander, said: "The transport submarines will be operating independently. They should be positioned to recover any crippled aircraft. I suggest they take up stations on the route from Oahu to the rendezvous point. If they can save the lives of a few fliers, it will be worth it."

Admiral Isoroku Yamamoto, Commander of

the Combined Fleet and architect of Plan Z: Operation Order Number One—the plan for the secret attack on Pearl Harbor—spoke: "It will be as Admiral Nagumo says. He is responsible and it will be his way."

The session in the main auditorium of the Imperial Naval War College in Tokyo had been going on for several days, and this was the last chance the personnel would have for an academic review of the tactical aspects of the attack.

Yamamoto made a signal and the overhead lights in the room came on. The huge scale model faded as a focal point. All attention shifted to the Admiral. "We are all very tired," he said. "This has been a demanding exercise. But now we must begin our work. We must go back now to our units and begin practice. Every man must know his duty. When the strike comes, each man must act like an automaton. I want the training so intense that any movement is a reaction, a natural, conditioned reflex. That way, the operation will be a success."

A feeling of relief permeated the room. All were bone tired after many days spent constantly reviewing the fleet route, the aircraft attack plan, and the method of escape. While the six aircraft carriers would have the battleships *Hiei* and *Kirishima* as well as three cruisers and nine destroyers as protection, the main hope was that the fleet could withdraw without engaging the American Navy. Going in, they would leave the island of Etorofu, swing north of the Kurile Chain, and use the fog cover caused by the Japanese currents along the 43rd Parallel. Being out of the usual shipping lanes, they should make it in undetected. Coming back, based on the results of the attack, they should know the counterstrike capabilities of the U.S. Navy, but, no matter, an evasive course would be taken so that the fleet would, hopefully, return without encountering any battle damage.

But there was also a feeling of tenseness in the auditorium, a result of the unanswered question: When?

Admiral Yamamoto looked around at his fellow officers and said quietly, "I do not know. I simply do not know."

None of the room pressed him, but the disappointment showed on their faces.

Yamamoto smiled. He explained: "We are military men. We have lived for many years executing the broad purposes of our Emperor and his government. I will share with you what I can. We have called you here with a purpose. This plan is an important part of the future of the Empire. I am not privy to all things that transpire or are planned, but we know, we all know, that conflict with the Americans is inevitable. Our colleague, Admiral Nomura, is in their capital, visiting their White House, meeting with their leaders, stalling for time. Well, as you know, we have done our part. The fleet is ready, our Naval Air Force is equipped and, possibly, he will have to stall no longer. I can tell you that important events are about to take place and you can easily guess what they are. I can also tell you, as your commander, we have only a few weeks in which to finalize the training of our men for this attack."

An audible sigh of pleasure and anticipation slipped into the room. Yamamoto smiled as he finished. "You will all know when the time is near. Events will be evidence of our future."

The men in the room all knew that their Admiral was telling them all that he could. They were

55

also aware that he had said more than he should. But they had picked up the gusto which had been intended and they were anxious to go to work. In proud anticipation, they began to stiffen to attention as Yamamoto said, "Go. Work. Prepare. I will see you soon."

Yamamoto left the conference room followed by only his two personal aides. As the door was pulled closed behind him, he heard the room burst into excited, fragmented conversations. As he walked down the corridor, he felt a warm glow of comradeship with the men he had just left, and he experienced the pulse of dedication that a military professional feels when he knows his men are committed to a goal.

They rode the brass cage elevator up to the third floor in silence. As Yamamoto strode toward his office, he saw the two armed, uniformed Army officers standing guard outside his office and adrenalin coursed through his body. Maybe the time for action had come. He knew the men by his door were aides to the War Minister, Hideki Tojo.

Entering his office, Admiral Yamamoto noticed that General Tojo had nearly filled the ash tray on the coffee table with well-smoked butts. The bald-headed General rose and extended his greeting to Yamamoto. With the bows of salutation over, the Admiral went and poured two drinks as he asked, "Do you want one?"

Tojo plopped back down onto the sofa and said, "I desperately need one. Please make it strong."

They asked about the health and comfort of each other's children. Courtesies exchanged, Tojo brought the conversation to a more serious subject. "I have just left Okawa and Suzuki. They asked me to come see you."

56

That was, Yamamoto knew, at least partially true. The Navy Minister, Admiral Okawa, lived under the compulsion to get to his official residence in Yokosuka by nightfall and, at that late hour, would be fussing with his driver to get out of Tokyo as soon as possible. On the other hand, General Suzuki, Chief of Planning for all the military, had a well-known aversion to coming to the Naval College because he did not want to offend his fellow Army officers. But, as far as Tojo being "asked" to come to Yamamoto, that was patently false: Tojo went where he wanted, when he wanted, and on his own initiative.

"How goes your climb up Mount Niitaka?" Tojo asked.

Yamamoto smiled broadly at the reference to the top secret code words that had been selected to launch the attack on Pearl Harbor. "We have climbed Mount Niitaka at least ten times in the past seven days," Yamamoto replied. "I am so proud of those men, General. They have such a sense of purpose. All they wait for is the orders to go."

The suggestion was not lost on Tojo. He had purposely not told the various commanders what the schedule was. Not the military commanders who would be going after the Philippines, Singapore, and Borneo; not the air forces which would be searching for the British Fleet in the Gulf of Siam and the Indian Ocean; and not the Naval men who would have to see to the southern Pacific and places like the Marianas, Solomons, and Gilberts. Everyone had been instructed to get ready, but no timetable had been formulated. In the overall plan, the attack on Pearl Harbor was just part of a massive effort, but it was pivotal. So, because of its importance, Yamamoto's plan was being given special and concerned attention. Tojo asked for a report on the war games that Yamamoto had just concluded. In only a few minutes, the War Minister felt the confidence that he had come to expect from briefing by Admiral Yamamoto. And, as it had been since the Pearl Harbor plan had first been initiated back in January, General Tojo was also infected with eagerness.

As Yamamoto finished, Tojo said, "Just this afternoon, several aides practically screamed for us to make a decision right now; others pleaded for a war decision. I cannot blame them; they are ready."

Yamamoto wanted desperately to ask: "When?" but he held his proper place and waited.

"Do You know," Tojo said, "there is a matter of being too ready?" Yamamoto nodded. Tojo continued, "But, I can tell you in confidence that the time is close enough that such a problem will not manifest itself."

"What about the diplomatic negotiations?" asked Yamamoto. The Japanese military held cabinet-level positions, appointed directly by the Emperor. They were not accountable to politicians but did not ignore politics.

Tojo smiled, "Prince Konoye is in there giving the necessary window dressing. He is doing all that is necessary to keep everyone guessing. The American Ambassador is an easy one for Konoye. Grew is so involved in his golf games and social dinners that he is diverted with no trouble. The Prince met with him last week and Toyoda is going to make another 'peace offer' next week. That should keep them busy for a while."

"But Grew is not a stupid man."

"No, no he is not," Tojo said. "But he is so sure

58

he can move mountains with his diplomatic charm that he has convinced himself that he can change the facts as he has already seen them. We picked up one of his telegrams in their so-called 'Brown' Code. He told Washington that he informed the Foreign Minister that the people of the United States could not give credence to our pledges and our explanations of our intentions. Now that is strong and could be effective, but then he turned right around and urged Toyoda to use his best efforts to prevent a further deterioration of relations. When they get that back in Washington, they will surely think there is still hope. He gives the constant impression that Prince Konoye is a real hope for peace."

"What an insult to the Prince," Yamamoto said.

"Well," Tojo said, "when the time is right, he will step aside and then we will see what the Americans think."

Yamamoto picked up the glasses and went to the bar again. Tojo asked that it be a weak one because he was going to have to leave in a few minutes. As Yamamoto was pouring from the heavy crystal decanter, Tojo said quietly, "We have decided on mid-December."

Yamamoto nearly dropped the decanter in his excitement. Tojo's famous grin appeared under his neatly trimmed mustache.

"It is the monsoon season that has forced the actual date," said Tojo, puffing out a long stream of tobacco smoke. "If we start later than that, our troops in Indo-China and all of Southeast Asia will be bogged down and possibly incur heavy losses in the rainy season."

Yamamoto beamed. "December weather will be excellent for all of the naval operations. Especially

59

the attack on Hawaii. The fogs up north will be heavy and offer excellent cover."

Tojo nodded. "Your calculations and observations have contributed to the plans. Our fuel resources will be at their optimum then; our men can be trained and transported easily. The time will be right."

"Will there be any chance of a change?"

Tojo shook his head. "No. What we are demanding of the Americans is not unreasonable. They and the Dutch, the French, and the English have expanded at their pleasure, but now, when we are looking for the good of all the peoples of Asia, they insist we are wrong. We are only demanding what is right, but they cannot accept it. On the other hand, their major demand, that we get out of China, is so easy for us to grant that it is silly. But still they keep insisting that we leave Manchukuo and that we cannot do. They can have China. We are wasting millions of dollars a day there. We'd leave right now, but they also want us out of what is historically ours—, Manchukuo. And we cannot have that. If they were prepared to grant that, there might not be war, but they do not, so there is no hope. None at all."

Yamamoto savored the news. Speaking almost wistfully, he said, "Mid-December. We have waited a long time."

Tojo nodded, then replied, "And we will move quickly. We are planning only two years to accomplish our objectives. By that time we will have won."

"That is a short time."

"Your combined fleet can do it. And your plan for the Americans will be a big step forward."

Yamamoto nodded humbly.

Tojo rose and said, "I must go now. People will

begin to chatter if I spend too long. Take care, Admiral, and work hard."

Yamamoto bowed. "I will work," he said, "as I have never worked in my life."

Outside evening was coming to Tokyo and the hot August air pushed down like a blanket over the city.

CHAPTER 7

TOKYO, JAPAN

AUGUST 14, 1941

Perspiration made Ambassador Grew's shirt cling to his body and damp stains were beginning to show under the sleeves of his seersucker suit. There was hardly a breeze in all of Tokyo, and not a whiff of air stirred inside the high walls of the Embassy compound. That unique fragrance of freshly cut grass floated up as the Ambassador inspected the meticulous manicuring that had been done by the gardeners late in the day.

"Had to have them work late. It would ruin the lawn to have it done in the midday sun. You understand that, don't you?" Grew spoke like a classroom instructor.

Ben Stockton replied with a quiet, "Yes, sir. I understand."

Grew turned slowly and looked at Ben. That nervous tic was already active in the Ambassador's neck. Suddenly, he asked, "Why was I not told? Who ordered that this be kept from me?"

Stockton rocked back and forth from toes to heels, trying to find words, but nothing would come out.

"What right do you have coming into my Embassy, lurking about like a spy, holding vital information from me? Believe me, young man, your career in the Foreign Service can be measured in weeks—if not days." He turned nervously away from Ben and busied himself with an unnecessary inspection of the garden.

At length, forcing the lump from his throat, Ben said quietly, "Sir, I had my orders. They came from the Undersecretary."

Grew spun around. "Welles? Right? You will both feel the wrath of the Secretary. You are an insolent, nefarious, contemptible Judas. I want you out of my Embassy."

The confrontation in the Embassy's garden had been set up earlier in the afternoon when Grew had first seen the *Japan Advertiser*. The English-language daily carried a story announcing the Roosevelt-Churchill meeting. Later, during cocktails, when Grew heard that Ben Stockton was furiously trying to get various Embassy secretaries to gather local reactions to the historic meeting, it became apparent just what Stockton's mysterious mission in Tokyo was. The Ambassador did not suppress his annoyance. Secretaries Chip Bohlen and Ned Crocker used their charm to calm Grew down and Stockton was summoned to meet the Ambassador in the garden at eight.

Ben was conciliatory. "Mr. Ambassador, it was felt that an unbiased report on the reaction was vital. There have been a lot of recent probes by the Japanese about our attitudes in the event of conflict between England and Japan. Some of the people in State feel there is a plan afoot for an invasion of British territories. The request came directly from the President to the Undersecretary."

Grew was not calmed. "I could have done that. That is my job. I have been diligent in keeping Washington informed. My hands have a firm grip on the overall climate here; no one knows that more than Frank."

Ben nodded, hiding his impatience. Grew was well known for incredibly long telegrams and despatches. He was on a first-name basis with Franklin Roosevelt and had a genius for always sending along a few valuable postage stamps to flatter Roosevelt's passion for philately. But there were always comfortable phrases interspersed in those communications, designed to indicate that all was well in the Empire of Japan, nothing to worry about, least of all war.

Stockton thought about one particular incident. Back in May, Grew had filed a despatch stating that the Minister of Foreign Affairs, Yosuke Matsuoka, had unequivocably stated that if the U.S. went to war with Germany, then Japan, under Article Three of the Tripartite Pact, would declare war on the United States. He had then watered down the threat with his own analysis of Matsuoka. "I rate him among my personal friends in Japan," he had written. The Foreign Minister's words were not to be taken seriously; it was all a sham.

This constant confusion of opinion coming from Grew had prompted the need for an on-the-spot overview in order to get a clear impression of the true state of affairs.

63

"Yes, sir," Stockton replied. "You could have done it; your analysis will be awaited. But I was sent here to observe also."

Grew pulled anxiously at his mustache. He would be expected to file a Tokyo reaction despatch quickly, but what if this brazen upstart from Washington came up with a counter opinion? What would that mean to Grew's career? The people back in Washington did not understand. Even the presence of Ben Stockton in the Embassy was an affront and, if the word ever got out among his Japanese colleagues, the effect would be devastating to all the hard work he had invested in building good relations with the anti-war faction within the Imperial government. Grew felt that his presence and skills had contributed to the strength of men like Prince Konoye, the Prime Minister. Grew believed that, thanks to his efforts, the militarists were being subdued and an equitable resolution, without appeasement, would be accomplished. Even now he was working desperately to arrange a meeting between President Roosevelt and Prime Minister Konoye; such a master stroke of diplomacy on his part would culminate all of his efforts and result in a peaceful solution to all of the problems that existed between Japan and the United States. An interloper like Ben Stockton could wreck all of those magnificent accomplishments.

". . . as soon as possible, Mr. Ambassador."

"What?" Grew was snapped out of his thoughts. "What did you say, Stockton?"

Ben repeated, "I will get my information and return to the States as soon as possible."

Grew was faced with an unenviable choice. To allow Stockton access to Japanese reaction might endanger the validity of his own report. But to prohibit overtly Ben from carrying out the assignment would be an admission of weakness, and a dangerous one. Grew could be seen to be sabotaging a State Department mission, authorized by Washington. It was something that could not be handled easily. He would need time to think the problem out.

"I will see you in the morning, Stockton. We will discuss the matter then."

"I need to start right now, sir. It is important to get impressions of the initial reactions to the announcement."

"Do what you will," Grew said, "but do not involve any of the staff. Is that clear?"

"But your men have contacts," Ben argued. "They could be invaluable in calling up Japanese that they know."

Grew ignored the plea. "Is that clear?" he said emphatically.

Ben sucked in a deep breath of air to dampen his anger. He nodded abruptly and stalked away from Grew.

As Ben approached the entrance to the Embassy dormitory, he noticed the Assistant Naval Attaché, Lieutenant Gruenwald, standing in the shadow of the doorway, smoking a cigarette. The Navy man said, "I've been waiting for you."

Bearing in mind Grew's instructions, Ben glanced around to see if anyone was watching. The area was clear except for the Ambassador himself, who was crossing the parking area and waving anxiously at one of the chauffeurs on duty. "What's up, Gruenwald?" Stockton asked as he kept an eye on Grew's movements.

"I'd like to talk to you. Off the record."

Ben nodded and pointed his index finger upward. "In my room?"

Ben heard the Ambassador's Lincoln start and a door slam as Grew climbed in. "Let's go," he said, leading the way toward the stairs to his room on the second floor.

Grew's car sped out of the compound.

Mack Priest's small house was about ten city blocks from the Embassy. By the time Grew arrived there, it was dusk.

Grew reached over the back seat and gestured to the Japanese driver to pull to the side of the road and park. The driver beamed, eased the car to a halt, and sing-songed, "I wait?"

Grew's concession to the Japanese language was a curt *"Hai."* In nine years, he had at least learned to say yes in the native tongue.

As with most inexpensive homes in Tokyo, Priest's house sat on a small plot of land surrounded by a six-foot-high wooden fence for privacy. Six feet provided an adequate barrier against the prying eyes of the diminutive Japanese, but Grew's tall frame allowed him to look right over. There were lights showing through the rice paper windows. The tiny garden in front was empty, but Grew could see rose clippings piled neatly by the front steps. That had been why Priest had slipped out of the Embassy earlier in the day: He had told Grew that he wanted to work on his beloved roses. Grew had agreed because Priest had been working especially hard during the absence of Eugene Dooman. Both Dooman and Grew had taken Priest on as a pet protégé, but he was not holding up at all well during the demanding absence of Dooman. Grew felt the break would provide a little necessary relaxation.

Grew let himself in the unlocked gate, walked quietly over the loose gravel of the entrance path, and stepped up onto the small porch. He rapped lightly and listened.

There was a scurrying, then a faint giggle, then Priest's voice called, "Just a minute." The words had been spoken in Priest's excellent Japanese so Grew had no idea what had been said. He rapped again.

Another rush of Japanese words came from inside and the inflection indicated there must have been curses of some kind.

Grew called in a soft voice, an octave or so lower than his normal range, "Mack?"

"Who the hell is it?" the voice came back in slurred, wavering English.

Grew did not answer. He could hear the shuffle of feet approaching the door. A bright light over the entrance flashed on and Priest yanked the door open.

Grew registered disapproval of the image in front of him. Mack Priest stood there with no shirt on, his hairy chest heaving in and out, his clothing a pair of soil-stained walking shorts. The zipper was open. The Ambassador took it all in—the man's grotesque shape, his paunchy belly hanging like a great balloon over the distended waist of his shorts. His feet showed black splotches of garden dirt between the toes.

"Maybe," the Ambassador said with obvious distaste, "maybe I should not have come."

Mack Priest broke into a huge grin and bellowed out, "Hey, Joe. Good to see you!" It dawned on the Ambassador that his underling was in his cups.

Grew turned to leave. "Sorry I bothered you," he said. But Priest lunged out the doorway and grabbed his boss by the arm.

"Hey, come-on-in. Nice-to-see-ya."

67

Mack's voice was loud, and Grew did not want the neighbors calling the police, so he slipped in and closed the door while he hissed his disapproval. "You're drunk, Mack."

"Hey," Priest blubbered, "nice of ya to use my first name . . . Joe."

Although Mack had been in Japan for several years, he had no special desire to live as a local, so his small house, while traditional in architecture and design, was cluttered with Western-style furniture.

Grew balked as Priest virtually dragged him toward the living room. He hated being touched and he deplored drunks, especially junior Embassy secretaries. As they stumbled into the room, Grew suddenly yanked his arm loose and jolted his body ramrod-erect. His neck began to jerk as he growled, "My God, Priest! Have you gone berserk?"

On the couch on the other side of the room was a Japanese girl clothed only in one of Mack's white shirts. Her legs were tucked up under her body, but the buttons on the shirt were not fastened and the gap was open all the way to her belly button.

Flustered, sputtering, bordering on rage, Grew gasped, "How old is she?"

"How about that, hey, Joe?" Priest weaved slightly, pointing a proud finger at the young girl.

Grew's eyes widened in anger. "Stop calling me 'Joe,' dammit." Then, looking back at the girl he repeated his question about her age.

Turning unsteadily to face the sideboard, Priest began pouring a drink of gin as he replied, "Her? My little Kazuko? Well . . . she's fifteen . . . I think."

"Good God, man. Are you insane?"

68

Priest lifted the glass and said, "She might be fourteen. I don't really know."

Grew summoned up his stern voice, the one he always used on his junior officers, and started to speak, but all he managed to get out was, "I have come here. . . ."

But Priest cut him off by saying, "Come on over here, Kazuko. Come meet my boss ... hic ... Joe."

"Stop that, Priest."

Mack's head rolled as he tried to focus on Grew. The Ambassador looked as if he were about to collapse as the tiny Japanese girl climbed off the couch and walked toward him.

She was a couple of inches short of five feet, but her body and legs—Grew could see everything through the loose drape of the shirt—were proportioned with perfection. Her face had the delicacy peculiar to young Japanese girls. To virtually any Westerner's eye, she would be beautiful.

Five steps from the Ambassador, she stopped, placed her feet together, and bowed from the waist as a greeting of respect. Out of habit, Grew made a cursory bow back, but he did not look at the floor as he should have. His eyes were riveted on the lovely barely formed mounds which were her breasts. Grew's wife, Alice, had been at the summer resort at Karuizawa for nearly a month and he had not been able to visit her; he felt a yearning. Shocked at his own natural reaction, Grew silently scolded himself as he said to Priest, "I came here to talk to you, Mr. Priest."

The formal address and the businesslike tone of voice fell on dead ears. Mack reached out his hand forward and cupped one of the small breasts in his hand. A leer disfigured Priest's face. "How about that, hey, Joe?"

Forgetting the neighbors for the moment, Grew raised his voice to a boom. "Get her out of here. I need to talk to you."

The harsh words showered on Priest like a spray of sobering ice water. He got half his glass of gin down in one gulp; the rest watered his gut. In urgent Japanese, he shooed the young girl into his bedroom.

Taking charge as he might have with a drunken roommate at Harvard, Grew moved Mack to the kitchen, doused his head with cold water and forced two glasses of milk down his throat. Back in the living room, Mack sat on the sofa, cradling his throbbing head between his shaking hands, and waited. Grew, aggravated by the unaccustomed duty, paused to collect his thoughts. As he did, he looked around the room. It was a mess. Dirty clothes were strewn everywhere and dishes covered with caked-on food sat on every flat surface. Off at a slight angle, Grew could see into Priest's bedroom. From his position, he could see about one-third of the room. The sheets and pillows were askew, the dresser was piled high with more dirty clothes, but the young girl was not in sight. With relief, Grew guessed that she had left while he was ministering to Priest in the kitchen. But he could not be sure. She might be hidden from sight. He would watch what he said.

"Gee, I'm really sorry," said Mack, his voice weak and apologetic.

Grew responded paternally. "You've been under a lot of strain." Then, not wanting to miss the moment for acting the regent, Grew scolded.

"How could you become involved with such a young girl?"

An evil, yet guilty, grin split Mack's face. "She works down the street at a florist I use. When you gave me the afternoon off, I went in to buy some rose bushes—you know how I love rose bushes—and she was nice to me. I've seen her there for several months and she's always been nice. Well, I suggested she stop by and see my flowers and. . . ."

Grew raised a pontifical hand to stop the flow of details. "We . . ." his use of the royal "we" was characteristic, "We must be discreet, Priest. Times are difficult."

Mack nodded an acknowledgment and forced a contrite gaze into his eyes.

Grew gave a satisfied smile and said, "We must work together on a critical problem, Mack."

Through his gin-haze, Priest gratefully accepted the first-name intimacy; he thrived on the crumbs thrown to him from Grew and the Embassy Counselor, Gene Dooman. Mack listened as Grew told of the important Roosevelt-Churchill meeting. Grew gave his view of the importance and then mentioned Ben Stockton's presence and mission.

Mack curled his lips in exaggerated disgust. "That sonovabitch," he spat. "I knew he was up to no good. Never did like that fucker coming here snooping around."

Grew nodded with condescending impatience and then told Mack what he wanted done. "You get yourself back into reasonable shape. I want you to be at the Embassy tonight. Get Crocker and Bohlen to pitch in but don't let them know what you are doing. You work like hell to help this Stockton. Make phone calls, go out and see

71

people, anything to make him feel that you are on his side. But, no matter what you learn, you tell him that the Japanese see the Roosevelt-Churchill meeting as very important."

Mack was slowly surfacing from his drunk. He agreed. "I'll bet they do think that."

Impatiently, Grew went on. "And you tell him that the news will greatly assist the efforts of the peacemakers in the government."

Mack's face started to offer a question but Grew hurried on. "Now listen to me. Don't interrupt. The announcement, I am sure, will give those damned militarists cause to reflect. I am sure they can be controlled. Now I want you to get that idea across to Ben Stockton. Then, when we file our despatch, all of the opinions will concur."

Mack was still silently quizzical.

Grew said, "Don't be an oaf, man. I can move this government of Konoye. He is like a child. He wants peace so badly that he will do anything. Believe me, I know what I'm doing."

Drunk or not, Mack could detect what he called "high-grade bullshit" when he heard it. "No one is going to believe that the military is scared of a U.S.-U.K. agreement. Those bastards are just itching to get into battle. With anyone."

Grew did not relish being lectured by a subordinate, drunk or sober. He exploded. "You have learned nothing. Now get this through your head: We can stop the Japanese. Maybe not forever, but surely for several more years. You just don't know, Mack. I move in circles that are foreign to you. There are strong forces for peace at work. The military is about to lose its position."

As he had for several years, Mack Priest swallowed his silent litany: "Bullshit, crap, garbage."

Then, as had become his usual way, he said, "I see, Mr. Ambassador. I didn't understand." Mack Priest knew that his future with the Foreign Service was totally in the hands of his two superiors, Grew and Dooman; he was not going to risk their wrath arguing about little matters like war and peace.

Calming himself noticeably, Grew smiled and said, "I'm glad you do, Mack. Really, you will see it all happen. As I so often like to remind my dear Alice, you are seeing history written. And Mack, remember that we will make our place in the records of this effort. We will maintain peace and provide one of the most glorious chapters in American diplomacy."

Mack wanted another drink. He had heard Grew manifest his self-appreciation so many times that it was a bore.

Grew's voice shifted into that mellow tone he used for dinner party chatter and he said, "Did you know that Alice's family has an extraordinary background in Japan?"

Mack had heard the story probably a hundred times: Grew had married Alice de Vermandois Perry, great granddaughter of Commodore Matthew Perry, the man who opened Japan to the U.S. in 1854. Grew frequently acted as though history had fated him for similar distinction.

Priest listened with closed ears, suffering through the wearily familiar speech. He distracted himself by studying the abstract composition of an overfilled ashtray on the coffee table in front of him. The pattern of butts and ashes was more interesting than the story. Because he was looking down at the mess, he did not see Grew's eyes as they glanced over toward the bedroom.

Grew kept talking; it was an easy rendition because he had developed the Commodore Perry talk over the years. It was good that he was speaking from memory because it would have been impossible for him to think of what to say in view of the distraction.

Mack's tiny plaything was standing in front of the dresser, brushing her hair. Had the view not been so startlingly attractive, Grew might have been upset that she had been in the bedroom all the time. Suppose she had heard what they said? Suppose she understood English? Suppose she was actually a spy for the Kempei, the military police? But no, that was not possible; she was so young . . . and so attractive.

She was standing sideways to Grew, and she stroked her hair slowly, sensuously, in an enticing way. Grew glanced guiltily over at Mack who seemed entranced by the ugly mound of cigarette ashes that had spilled onto the lacquered coffee table. Grew sneaked a peek back toward the bedroom. He saw that the girl had switched hands with the hairbrush and, because of the changed position, the man's shirt she was wearing had parted so that her entire front was excitingly exposed. Grew thought he was watching undetected until she turned her head toward him and flashed a warm smile. Caught, and embarrassed, Grew snapped his eyes away and looked back at Mack. As Grew continued his Perry narrative, he saw that Priest was still not aware that the girl was visible. He moved only his eyes as he looked back into the bedroom. The girl offered another inviting smile, then brought her tongue out and brushed it across her lips. Grew allowed himself a quick, nervous smile. The girl stopped brushing. She took her free hand and moved it slowly to her body. First she slid it over her breast, then down over her incredibly flat stomach. The movement of her hand was rhythmic and Grew watched the performance in fascination. He had no idea how long he had watched her; his only measure of time was that he had mechanically arrived at the point where he was talking about the Perry Expedition Celebration back in 1934. He cut the story off and said, "Say, Mack, do you mind if I use your facility?"

"Huh?"

"I'd like to go to the bathroom if that is more understandable." Grew smiled through his arrogance.

Mack snapped himself back into the conversation. "Sure. It's through the bedroom."

From the couch, Mack could not see into the bedroom, but he did see the shadow of his playmate moving around. Priest might not have been the most astute Foreign Service Officer in the business, but he was an expert on most matters concerned with sex. It required only a couple of seconds to realize that Grew must have seen the half-naked girl in the bedroom and might be interested in getting another look.

"Hey, sure, Mr. Ambassador. You go right ahead."

The tone of his voice was overly solicitious. Furthering his point as brazenly as possible, Mack said, "Listen, you just go ahead and use anything you want. You get my point ... anything here is yours to use. Okay?"

Grew went stuffy. He did smile as he said, "I'll just be a minute."

Seeing a beautiful chance to curry favor with the most important man in his life, Mack said, "Take as long as you want. I'll fix me something to eat in the kitchen. Then I'll get ready to go back to the Embassy. Take your time."

Grew moved across the room and slid the door closed behind him.

The girl standing there, the shirt parted widely, her childlike body gleaming in the bright light of the room.

"Eh. Good evening . . . eh . . . Miss."

With exquisite slowness the girl stared up at Grew with warm brown eyes. In nearly a whisper, she said, "You rike Kazuko? That me . . . Kazuko. You rike?"

Grew's bushy eyebrows came close together as he let a slight smile slip onto his face. Gently, he said, "You are a very attractive young lady . . ."

Ben Stockton took two more bottles of Kirin beer from the small cooler under the wash basin and handed one to Lieutenant Gruenwald.

"So, okay," he said, slumping onto his narrow bed. "What do you want from me?"

They had been talking through the first beer and a half a pack of Camels. Gruenwald told him that Commander Smith-Hutton, the Naval Attaché, had pretty well decided that the missing ONI man was dead. Operating as quietly as possible, the Naval and Commercial Attachés had poked around in Kobe, Osaka, and Kyoto, and, because every trail they picked up led quickly to a dead end, they had to assume the worst. In four days there had been not one trace of the ONI man. The business, military and police authorities were so overly solicitous that the assumption of death had to be made. If the agent had been arrested or was being held, the Japanese would be making great noises about it because that was their style. Back in 1932, the Japanese police had caused a major incident in Osaka by prohibiting publicity photographs to be taken by the American-owned National City Bank; charges bordering on espionage had been made that time. There had been dozens of incidents since then, like the time Frank Schuler had been Vice Consul in Kobe. He wanted to walk the long, ancient pilgrimage route from Kyoto to Tokyo just to get a feeling for some Japanese history; his walk had caused a furor and he was questioned by police. The Japanese, contrary to appearances, were not paranoid about foreigners. They were, however, masters at turning a minor incident into a heavy propaganda vehicle. If the missing ONI man had been involved in the death of a respected geisha, headlines would be screaming out the news.

"We know you're going back to the States soon," Gruenwald said, "and, because you're not staying here, we'd like to ask for some help. If the thing goes wrong, then the Embassy won't lose one of it's regular staff."

Ben took a swig of beer. "Sounds ominous."

The young Naval Intelligence officer smiled and said, "Not really. More like a messenger's job."

Stockton felt that Gruenwald was playing with him; they had not just gone through a long exposition of the mission being carried out by the ONI agent so that Ben could be talked into a simple messenger job.

Ben said, "Why don't you lay it out and then let's see."

"We want you to go to Kyoto," was the abrupt opener. "We want you to pick up the agent's belongings."

Ben cocked his head sarcastically. "Just like that? Why me?"

"Because you're available."

"Not good enough."

"Look," Gruenwald said, "the ONI man was under a deep cover; nobody from Navy can show interest. The Commercial Attaché has to keep his hands off because he has already been told that the authorities know nothing. We're not looking for you to go pull a Mr. Keene; we just want you to go pick up his personal effects. We've written the guy off, but he might have left something in his things at the hotel. The Japs will only give them to a diplomatic representative. That's it. We need help."

" 'Written him off,' that's pretty casual, isn't it? Maybe the guy is on a binge."

Gruenwald shook his head. "Wrong. He was an excellent agent. If he was alive, he'd have gotten a signal to us. There's nothing. The poor bastard is probably being eaten by crabs at the bottom of Lake Biwa right now. Why not make his death worth something? He might have left some message in his hotel room."

Stockton mulled the problem over through several gulps of beer and a couple of puffs of his cigarette. "Shit," he said, "do you know what Grew'd say if he found out?"

"We can't bring him into it, Ben. Do you have any idea what he'd do if he even thought we were running a covert operation out of *his* Embassy. Hell, he'd have apoplexy. We'd all get bounced out of here."

"Sure," said Ben. "What that means is that I'm expendable. If the Ambassador happens to get highly pissed off at me, that's okay. But you and the Commercial people come up clean."

Gruenwald paused before he acknowledged Ben's masterly analysis of the situation. Ben stubbed a finger at him. "Well, I think that's pretty shitty."

Gruenwald slammed his beer bottle down on Ben's small writing desk. "Listen, Stockton. One damned fine young Naval officer has gotten his ass knocked off trying to do a job for all of us. Now quit thinking about yourself and worrying about Grisly Joe Grew. You're the best one to get us the stuff, so quit screwing around."

Gruenwald was right and Stockton knew he was right. What difference did it make if Grew got upset? There was going to be a major protest sent from the Ambassador to Secretary Hull about Ben even being in Tokyo; one more complaint would make no difference.

"Sorry, Lieutenant. I see what you mean."

Stockton was settled down in his first-class compartment as the train for Kyoto pulled out at 10:30 that night. A possible confrontation with Ambassador Grew was only one of the many things on his mind as he began the seven-hour train ride.

CHAPTER 8

WASHINGTON, D.C.

SEPTEMBER 5, 1941

"I saw it, Frank, saw it there in his own hand-writing."

"Rainbow?"

"Right."

"That's more proof," said Frank Schuler.

"Shit," said Ben Stockton.

Stockton had arrived back in Washington the previous Friday night after the strenuous trip across the Pacific, then the continent.

Frank Schuler, working in the Department of State's Far Eastern Division on the Japan desk was, in the fraternal jargon of the department, one of the "old Japan hands." Starting out in 1931 as Vice Consul at the Consulate in Kobe, he had become a Third Secretary in the Tokyo Embassy in 1937. Since transferring back State-side, he had worked continuously on the Japan desk. Nearly everyone who came home from Japan made a point of getting together with Frank within a few days of returning. Frank and Ben were meeting in the coffee shop of the Mayflower Hotel.

"You'd better watch it with those donuts," Stockton chided him.

It was a standing joke within the Far Eastern Division that Olive, Frank's bride, hounded him about his addiction for the Mayflower Coffee Shop donuts. But that gag found a home in nearly every government office in the District because the donuts were famous.

Frank smiled but came back to the subject. "What did Grew have to say?"

Ben pounded the heel of his hand against his forehead. "What didn't he say? Those bastard cops in Kyoto. The first thing they did was to call the Embassy. Fortunately, they got Crocker who tried to cover for me, but Priest got into the act and he went running tattle-tale to Grew and all shit hit the fan. But while we were waiting, I conned the police sergeant into letting me see the personal effects. There were two letters, both phoney as hell. One to the toy company, the other to an 'aunt' in San Francisco. It was obviously in code, but big as hell, there was Rainbow."

"Rainbow Five" was the project code phrase used to identify the maximum effort defense of the U.S. Naval Base at Pearl Harbor. Naturally, when Stockton had discovered that phrase in the two letters written by the dead Navy undercover agent, all sorts of warning flags had begun waving.

"The bastards wouldn't let me have them though," Ben explained. "They said they'd have to hold them for 'investigation.'"

"Did Smith-Hutton say anything about the other parts of the letters?"

"I didn't work with Smith-Hutton," said Ben. "I think he stayed as far from the whole thing as possible. You know, he's got to live with Grew for a long time."

Frank munched into another honey-flavored donut. "He hates Grew's ass though. He told me

Grew is dangerous as hell in his light treatment of the Jap military."

"Well, no matter, I worked with an ONI guy, Lieutenant Gruenwald."

"Don't know him."

"He arrived about a year ago. After you left, I guess."

"What'd he say?"

Ben took a sip of coffee. "He blanched when I mentioned what I could remember from reading the letters. The Jap police in Kyoto only let me read them each once, so I probably missed a lot. But he was concerned as hell about the use of the word."

"I guess so," Frank agreed. "It's a shame they couldn't get the letters and decode them."

"They must have been written before he went to see his geisha; too damned bad he didn't post them."

Frank lifted the remains of his third donut and said, "They would have grabbed them anyway. If the ONI agent was that close to the end, the letters would have been intercepted at the post office." He swallowed the last morsel.

Ben Stockton was tired. The trip back to Washington had not been restful, even though he was trapped on a transPacific passenger ship for fifteen days between Yokohama and San Francisco. His departure had been inauspicious; Ned Crocker had taken him to the ship after Grew had spent nearly three hours on one of his favorite "send-off" lectures. Grew pleaded for his peaceful point of view. He returned constantly to his prevailing theme: Only the militarists want war with the U.S. Grew tried to enlist Stockton in the cause of support for the Konoye government: With men like the Prince as Prime Minister, the Emperor would force the military into line because, of all the people in Japan, His Imperial Majesty was the most peace loving. Grew always emphasized this by referring to the splendid dinners he had frequently had with Tenno Heika, the Japanese familiar for their Man-God ruler. Grew equated interesting dinner chatter about flowers, fish, and golfing with the good intentions of gentlemen. The Emperor liked the United States and so be it. Stockton had left the lecture feeling drained; emotionally it was difficult to listen to such clap-trap after thinking about the ruthlessness of the killers of the young ONI agent. The two images would not mesh together comfortably. The drained feeling stayed with Ben all the way home and it hung with him as he talked with Frank Schuler.

"I've got to acknowledge one thing," Ben admitted. "He did turn his troops loose on the Roosevelt-Churchill reaction. Crocker, Bohlen, Espy; all of them got out and picked up initial Japanese reactions. That was why I was there in the first place."

"What'd they turn up?" Frank asked.

"A mixed bag," Ben replied. "Everything from 'not important' to 'threat of war.' Generally though, the Atlantic Charter was not considered a hindrance to negotiations for peace between the U.S. and Japan."

Frank waited for Ben to continue, but there was nothing else. The two men sat there. Frank glanced out through the window and saw Oklahoma Senator Kerr talking with Texas Congressman Sam Rayburn. He smiled as he watched the two men chatting and tipping their hats at passersby. "I wonder what oil tax concession they're mulling over."

Ben, new to Washington, lost the point of the crack and waited for Frank's reaction. When Schuler said nothing, Ben asked, "Well, what do you think?"

"I think you've been had."

"Hey, wait a minute," Ben challenged. "I might not be as savvy as some of you 'old Japan hands,' but I sure as hell know that Crocker and Bohlen wouldn't bullshit me."

"You talked to each one of them?"

Ben shook his head in disbelief. "Look, I know Grew might have his own strong views, but he'd never actually put bias into a report."

"Who'd you talk to?"

Ben was getting angry. He said curtly, "Priest."

"That's all?"

"Look, Frank, I know what you're suggesting. But I confirmed a couple of the opinions. Listen, give the devil his due, Grew and Priest got the staff digging. They must have talked with a hundred or more people. Priest condensed the whole mass of information and gave a digest. Priest is no dummy, Frank. He might be a slob, but he is a bright guy."

"Mack is a bright guy," Frank acknowledged, "but he is also a lackey of Grew and Dooman. Priest wants a career in the Foreign Service; he can ensure it through Grew. I'm not saying that Ned or Chip or this Espy guy—I don't know him too well—would falsify what they dug up. I do think that Grew would force Priest to look at the analysis from only one point of view. Joe Grew is determined to promote his 'peace-is-possible' contention. Personally, I feel he is capable of forcing the facts to fit that mold."

Ben mulled that for a moment, then agreed. "He is pretty obstinate about the Schreiber tip."

Frank had been on duty at State in Washington when the Pearl Harbor warning despatch had arrived by pouch from Tokyo back in February. His wife, Olive, was working in the Department at that time. She too had seen Grew's message. They had talked about it and at first treated it with the casualness induced by Grew's last line: "The Embassy places no credence in Schreiber's story." That was the prevailing reaction to the report given by the Peruvian Minister in Tokyo. But Frank had second thoughts provoked by some of the subsequent despatches and telegrams; he had begun to change his thinking about the Pearl Harbor tip. Some of Grew's opinions were radically different from those he had formed on the basis of his own experience in Japan. Serious doubts began to collect in his mind.

"Schreiber's a good man," said Frank. "I met him when he first arrived in '38."

Stockton agreed. "I met him. He seems sincere as hell. He also tipped me off that the Imperial Navy is running through war games that include an attack on Pearl."

"We've gotten some minor vibrations about that; but nobody can pin it down to anything more than backstairs gossip. I wouldn't be surprised, though."

Ben asked, "What do you think about Schreiber's tip?"

Frank toyed with the idea of another donut. "Schreiber's a good man and means well, but, in the end, I guess we have to go with Grew's assessment. Remember Schreiber sounded awfully urgent back in January and nothing has happened yet. Grew's view of 'no credence' has to be accepted."

Ben grimaced in frustration. "There's so much bullshit flying around, it's hard to believe anybody."

"Have you heard about the plans for a Roosevelt-Konoye meeting?" Frank asked.

"No."

"Wilfrid Fleisher broke the story in the *Herald Tribune* yesterday. It might be possible."

Ben's spirits jumped. "That would be great."

Frank corrected him. "That would be a disaster."

"How so?"

"Two things," Frank replied. "It would give the Japs time to really build up their fighting units and it would lull everyone into thinking that there was hope for peace."

"But the oil embargo would hurt hell out of their Navy," Ben argued. "I saw one ONI report that said their ships are using 400 tons of oil an hour! That's a hell of a lot of oil."

Frank nodded. "You are missing one small point: The Japs knew damned good and well that the oil embargo was coming, so they simply ordered all the oil companies to increase their reserves. They've got enough engine fuel in Japan to last for two years."

Ben looked shocked. "Then why the hell the embargo?"

Frank gave an ironic smile. "Ask the H-Boys: Hull, Hornbeck, and Hamilton. They seem to think they can bluff the Japs and that's what they've been feeding up to Roosevelt."

"Even *I* can see that the Japs won't be bluffed; who are they kidding?"

"No one really," Frank replied. "We all pretty

well agree that the Japs are going to move; it's just that our bosses are convinced that the inevitable can be delayed for a few years."

Ben gave a laugh that caused several people in the coffee shop to look. Then, quietly, he said to Frank, "I ain't no great shakes in analysis, but it would take an imbecile not to see that the Japs are tough and won't be bluffed too easily. Why doesn't Grew put them straight?"

"Oh," Frank answered, "Grew sends the stuff along. But he colors it with his pontifications about the 'peace factions,' then, when Hornbeck and Hamilton get through with their mastication, the items go on upstairs with any vital information slipped in at the end as 'Minority Position.' Hell, who's going to even glance at something hidden there."

Ben shook his head. "I've got a hell of a lot to learn."

Frank smiled and said, "I've got ten years in and I'm still learning. The most important thing is don't get trapped by the system."

Ben made a mock show of horror and said, "That's heresy."

"It'll change."

"How? Not with Secretary Hull?"

"No," Frank answered, "not with our gentleman from Tennessee. He's too wedded to the old school. But there are people who will break the system."

"You sound like a rebel," said Ben.

"Not really. Times are changing, but our State Department is lagging. Look, there's a reason for men like Hull and Hornbeck and Hamilton keeping the Department small. If they have to go up to the Hill and ask for expansion money, Congress is going to begin looking into operations. A next logical step would be to look into policy procedures, then the whole thing would begin to change. It is to the advantage of the Old Guard to hold the status quo. That's why State's budget requests are constantly low while all other departments' are exploding."

"But surely FDR can see this."

"FDR has had eight years of trying to get this country back on its domestic feet. He's had a War Department crying for fantastic budget increases, and he has been waging a demanding battle against the America-First people. I don't think the President has had a lot of time for quiet introspection. Hull has been running State nice and quiet; FDR is happy as hell with that."

Ben was reluctant to accept the argument. "But he's not a fool," he protested.

Frank replied impatiently. "Of course he's not a fool, Ben. But State has caused no disasters for FDR, so he is comfortable with Hull. But he is not blind; you know that. Why do you think the President has been working with Welles? The Undersecretary has some great ideas and FDR is going to let him go ahead; but not at the expense of Hull."

Ben had great respect for Sumner Welles. It was the Undersecretary who had formed the cadre of troubleshooters to which Ben belonged, but Hornbeck and Hamilton had always been so successful in watering down the cadre's findings that Ben often felt he was not contributing anything of real value.

Frank said, "You've seen it in operation. Joe Grew is one of the Old Guard. You've come up against him, and I think he put one over on you this time. That's the way the system really functions."

"It's insidious. Why the hell are we fighting each other?"

Frank began to pull himself up out of his seat as he said, "That, my boy, is the name of the game: Power Politics." Then, he added, "I've got to get home to Olive. She's really put out with me about the Claughton thing tonight. A going-away party. Are you coming?"

Ben shook his head. "I'm catching the eight o'clock train to New York. Welles is with Hull at Hyde Park. I've got to go give a report."

Frank exaggerated his reaction as he picked up the check. "Ohhh, a summons to Olympus."

Ben dropped a tip on the table and replied, "I am a mere messenger of the Gods. And," he added sarcastically, "it looks like all I am doing is parroting the views of the Great God Grew. I really feel like a dupe."

Frank led the way out. "We all have our bad moments in life, Ben. Just be on guard the next time."

They said their good-byes on Connecticut Avenue. Frank took his car and drove to his apartment in the Broadmoor; Ben caught a cab to Union Station.

At precisely the time Frank was leaving his apartment to go out with his chums at State, and Ben was sitting in his Pullman seat as the train pulled out of the station, the Imperial Conference was meeting in the West Wing of the Emperor's Palace in Tokyo. During the meeting, Prime Minister Konoye would make a weak, tentative case for continuing negotiations for peace with the Americans; War Minister General Tojo would then state the military's position in regard to war materials, troop morale and a possible timetable. After hearing Tojo's cryptic, forceful comments, the Emperor commented, *"Ah-so-desuka."*—"I see how it is." That day, the Imperial Council made the fateful decision: War with the U.S. if some acceptable diplomatic settlement was not reached by the beginning of October.

CHAPTER 9

HYDE PARK, N.Y.

SEPTEMBER 6, 1941

The living room at the south end of the Roosevelt home in Hyde Park was large and bright. A log burned in the fireplace at the west end of the room because a chilling, early fall frost had settled over Dutchess County.

Secretary of State Cordell Hull sat uneasily in the overstuffed armchair before the fireplace. FDR's pet Scottie, Fala, did not make Hull any more comfortable curled up beside him; Hull found it repugnant for a dog to have such freedom in a home. Back in Tennessee, it was acknowledged that a dog had some place in life but that place was out in a field hunting. Once, several years before, Hull had presumptuously said to the President: "A dog exists very well out in a yard." FDR replied without rancor, but firmly: "Ah, my dear Hull, that is just the point;

90

Fala is not a dog." The matter was not broached again.

Hull could hear FDR's mother, Sara Delano, giving the staff instructions in her small, pink-accented sitting room down the main hallway. The mother was a part of FDR that Hull could understand; she was a lady of the old order. She ran the home well, deported herself in a proper manner, and had used all of her extensive family influence to help her son progress. To Hull's mind, FDR would be a magnificent President if he could only emulate the style and manner of his mother. FDR thought otherwise. Hull had accepted the Roosevelt way and his acquiescence had led the former Congressman from Tennessee to the State Department.

Hull did not look up as he heard the flurry of activity far down the hall, but he knew the President had just come down the small elevator from the second floor; there was always a minor ruckus getting FDR's wheelchair up that small step leading to the entrance foyer.

FDR's voice boomed into the living room. "Hull, good morning. What the hell are you doing in that suit? This is a working farm, you know."

As a matter of fact, Cordell Hull had, on a few occasions, found immense delight in "messing around in the dirt" on FDR's Hyde Park estate. When the property had been improved years before, Roosevelt had deemed that it should be a working farm in perpetuity in order to retain some of the heritage of the early farms in Dutchess County. A part of the land would forever be dedicated to agriculture. Of course, a museum had been opened the summer before and it was difficult to reconcile the image of aggressive agriculture with the depository of FDR's mementos, but the building did look somewhat like a stone farmhouse if visitors did not look too hard. FDR got a kick out of making Hyde Park available to the voters.

"I've got to get back to Washington, Franklin," the Secretary responded. "There'll be no sod-busting for me today."

Roosevelt was dressed in gray flannel trousers, an open-necked shirt, and a dark blue sweater. This bothered Hull. Appearances mattered to him: It did not seem right for the President to lounge around in old clothes.

"Nonsense," FDR boomed back. "You'll stay another day."

Hull started to protest, but the President had yanked on the wheels of his chair and spun around heading down the hall. As he passed his mother's sitting room, he called in, "Morning, Mommie," then, back to Hull, he called, "Come on for breakfast."

The dining room was much to Hull's liking, but again it conflicted with his idea of presidential propriety. The table was heavy, utilitarian oak, the chairs and service sideboards sturdy and attractive, but not the grand, highly polished mahogany that would more seemingly befit the highest office in the land. Hull shuddered at the thought of FDR entertaining European royalty in this simple setting; Hull had no way of knowing it, but royalty tend not to be snobs. FDR did know.

FDR ordered breakfast, spicing the menu with side comments to Hull. "Eggs and sausage . . . so why do you need to leave us . . . with some of those oranges Senator Pepper sent us from Florida . . . I can see no reason for your going . . . and toast with jam . . . I want to talk to you about the Japs ... the strawberry jam that we preserved ... I'm worried about that, you know ... and a pot of tea ... you'll drink tea, Hull?"

"Coffee, please."

"Ahh, that's right," FDR beamed. "Coffee for the Secretary, with ... chicory, isn't that how you like it?"

"Yes, please," said Hull. "I'll settle for some toast."

Roosevelt laughed. "And some of Senator Pepper's orange juice, Hull. You can't offend my good friend from Florida."

Hull had never particularly cared for Senator Claude Pepper from Florida, but Pepper was close to FDR and he also sat on important Senate committees. Hull indicated tepid enthusiasm for orange juice.

Looking out the window across the wide lawn that ran down toward the Hudson River, FDR became contemplative. "You know, Cordell, it is terrible to live in critical times. There are so many damn things we can ball up. If you're right, you're down in the books with Washington and Abe Lincoln. If you're wrong, you're up there with Calvin Coolidge and Donald Duck."

Hull did not care to get philosophical. He wanted to get back to Washington. "The Japanese matter, Mr. President?"

FDR grinned broadly, took a cigarette from the small box by his place. As he lit it, he said, "Relax, we have the whole day."

"I must get back to. . . ."

"You can stay a while," said the President. "State can look after itself for a couple of hours. Or is someone likely to declare war on us today, Mr. Secretary?"

"I doubt it, Mr. President."

The President sipped his orange juice. "I did a lot of thinking last night, Hull, and I remembered something from way back in my undergraduate days at Harvard. I had a classmate—I can't remember his name, but I could look it up. He was a Japanese. Well, you know the way young collegians talk and chat. We were no different. This young man—I think his name was Kashu-something—no matter, he told me that he knew of a plan back in his country, a plan of conquest that might take a hundred years. But, when it was accomplished, Japan would have conquered dozens of countries including ... now hear this ... Panama, Mexico, and even Peru."

Hull arched his snow-white eyebrows over the rim of his orange juice glass. "Absurd," he said.

The rest of breakfast arrived. As the maid left the room, FDR said, "Now don't go pompous on me. Remember the Zimmerman incident?"

Hull remembered. He had been a freshman Congressman when the story broke. The Japanese had been accused of plotting to assist a Mexican invasion of the United States in 1914. It had been dismissed as British-inspired propaganda. Nevertheless, there had been some evidence of Japanese animosity toward America. Still, Hull said, "It was far-fetched."

Roosevelt spoke as he devoured his breakfast. "Remember the time frame, Hull. Japan had knocked Russia on her Czarist ass, while she was trying to establish her presence in Manchuria and she had annexed Korea. Now that little island empire was strong. It is perfectly possible that my schoolmate knew what he was talking about."

Hull did not respond.

FDR went on. "Even if he was a braggart or overimaginative, he impressed me and, you know, he might have known what he was talking about. I'll tell you this: I know damn well the Japs are out for conquest, and lots of it."

"Mr. President," Hull said, "it is obvious that they have too many people and too little living space and that they are after land and resources. I do think they have limits to their hopes though. I think they'll stop once they have a source of oil, and I'm nearly certain they will not attack us unless it is in the Philippines."

"Why not?"

"Primarily, because we have nothing to offer them. The United States is too far away."

"My God, man, they're closer to the Philippines than we are."

"Who ever heard of a nation going to war out of desperation?"

Roosevelt raised a hand in protest: "I did. That's Hornbeck's line you're preaching, isn't it?"

Hull nodded. His advisor on the Far East, Dr. Stanley Hornbeck, had used those exact words to prove the impossibility of Japan attacking the United States. Hornbeck was the principal inspiration of those men in the Department of State who rejected the possibility of war with Japan.

Roosevelt went on. "I've never held much with his argument, Cordell. Germany's rampage in Europe right now is, I feel, motivated by desperation."

"They're all madmen in Germany," Hull came back.

"Mad or not, they're getting room to spread out and they're getting control of natural resources. Just the things you said Japan needs."

Hull protested. "Japan is different. There is a small faction of militarists who have been getting their way in insignificant matters. The people of Japan are getting tired of the losses in China. Japan has lost many young men and is spending too much money there. If we can just stall them, the military's power will collapse under the strain at home."

The President dissented. "The Jap military is pretty strong. They have gotten a ton of money to build up their navy, they have been producing aircraft at a startling rate and, to be honest, they've taken over some places that are quite productive as far as income is concerned. The military is a threat and our own intelligence boys are getting a little edgy."

Hull was ready for that ploy; Hornbeck had briefed him. "Our own military are acting just like the Japanese. I am reluctant to call Stimson or Marshall 'war-mongers,' but darn it, Franklin, they are pushing us to the cliffs on this one. If the War Department keeps pushing, the militarists in Japan will get control over the Emperor."

Roosevelt had finished eating. He lit another cigarette. "Your point is well taken and I think you know that General Marshall is doing all he can and is taking your advice. One point though, and maybe you can clarify this for me: If the Japanese militarists are so powerless, and if they don't now control the Emperor, why are they so successful with their projects and why, please tell me, why is it that in every photograph I see of that Hirohito person, he is in full military regalia? Hell, Cordell, I am Commander-in-Chief but you don't see me wearing my admiral's uniform." Then, with a smirk, he added, "As much as I'd love to."

Hull smiled, too. Roosevelt had been Assistant

Secretary of the Navy, and everyone knew of his deep love for the sea.

Weakly, Hull responded, "I guess the Emperor just likes to wear uniforms."

Roosevelt poured himself another cup of tea. "I'd like to meet him," he said.

Hull blanched. The prospect of a high-level meeting with the Japanese had been under consideration for quite a long time. State was violently opposed.

"Franklin, that would be the worst thing that could possibly happen. Everyone from Hornbeck on down has voiced opposition to that strategy. Until we can get some solid basis for you to have a discussion, I feel it is imperative to reject any such idea. We have no basis for a meeting."

Roosevelt's opinion of personal diplomacy and his faith in himself in dealing with international situations was high. The recent Churchill meeting had been engineered by FDR's friend and close advisor, Harry Hopkins. "Do you want me to get Hopkins to pop over there and try to set up some basis for a meeting?" Roosevelt asked.

Hull felt ill again. The last thing he wanted was to have an "outsider" meddling in the affairs of his department. Responding anxiously, Hull said, "We can handle it, Mr. President. Grew is working very hard there, and I am having regular meetings with their Ambassador."

"Come on with me," Roosevelt said as he wheeled himself out the door. In a couple of minutes, they were moving along the paths through the expansive gardens. The sun had taken the biting chill off the morning, but it was still cool.

"Isn't this lovely?" Roosevelt said as he drank in the richness of the beautifully maintained garden. Then, without giving Hull time to respond, he asked, "What's Grew up to over there?"

"He is working very hard. I think he is doing a terrific job."

Roosevelt stopped by an especially large rose bush. "You should see this when it's in bloom," he said. "I'm sure Joe Grew is functioning as a good ambassador should. Look, Cordell, I like Grew. He is a fine man and he's like a magpie when it comes to finding superb stamps for my collection. But times are pressing in on us. I know Joe places great import on his dinners and his social activities. I know he feels very important about being the dean of the diplomatic corps in Tokyo. But he also might be distracting himself from the problem. Now I want us to avoid getting into a shooting mess with the Japs. I'd like to see Grew get out of his social rut over there and start bumping ass with some of the important people. If that means the military, then so be it. We've got to know what's going on."

Hull looked as if he had just stepped in a pile of horse manure. He hated bad language and the thought of one of his Ambassadors breaking with protocol pleased him not at all.

"I'll send off a telegram to him when I get back."

FDR let his anger show. "Now don't you start playing with me, Hull. We've been handling this as a team and it will continue that way. Joe Grew is our man in a very tough spot. All I am suggesting is that he might get close to the military and see what they are up to. I am not trying to run your department."

Secretary Hull was getting old and his circulation was not the best. He was cold. As they moved back to the house, they saw that several of Hull's aides had gathered.

"It looks like your people are anxious about moving," said Roosevelt.

"We have a lot of work to do in Washington," Hull admitted.

"Okay, you head on back," said the President. "I'll be down tomorrow and we'll talk more about the Japs." He paused. Still out of earshot of the group gathered on the large front veranda, FDR said, "Get me some solid information. I need it."

"I am doing my best, Mr. President," said Hull.

Ben Stockton tossed his small suitcase back up onto the luggage rack as he stared out the window of his train.

He had spent the night at the Commodore Hotel and had caught a special section of a New York Central train that was going to Hyde Park, then returning instead of going on to upstate New York. Stockton saw why the train was turning around at Hyde Park. The Secretary of State and his entourage of about thirty were leaving to go to Washington.

There, by the passenger platform of the small Hyde Park station, was President Roosevelt, sitting behind the wheel of his special Ford Phaeton, a four-door convertible equipped with special controls to allow him to indulge his love of driving. He had led a procession of seven autos from the residence to the station and he seemed in good spirits. Ben could see he was going to miss his visit to the famous private home of the President. Secretary Hull was standing by the President's car as Stockton moved to the vestibule.

The first member of the party to board the train was Maxwell Hamilton, Chief of the Far

Eastern Division in Washington. Hamilton's eyes lighted on Stockton. "What the hell are *you* doing here?" he exploded.

Ben was startled by the challenge; the orders for him to travel to Hyde Park had come from Hamilton's assistant. He was thinking up a suitable answer when Hamilton shoved him back into the Pullman car.

Hamilton screamed: "I asked what the hell are you doing here!"

Ben could match Hamilton's anger. "You ordered it, goddamn it," he said.

Hamilton threw his heavy leather briefcase onto the seat. "What do you mean?" he roared. "Did I tell you to come here? Did I telephone you or leave you a message?"

"No, but...."

Hamilton raged. "Did I tell you in any way whatsoever that you were to come here?"

"Your goddamned assistant said you wanted me here to brief you and Hornbeck on Japan."

Hamilton calmed down some. His face was a little less the color of tomato soup, his jaw a little less like a sprung bear trap. "There now," he said. "I'm glad you admitted your error. *I* didn't tell you nor did *I* order you to come here. You might try a little more precision when you are in such a critical area of government as we are."

Hamilton then proceeded to give him a couple of minutes of one of his lectures on the critical necessity for exact language. Stockton had heard of it, but this was the first time he had caught the full direct attack of Hamilton's irrationality.

"I will want you to brief Dr. Hornbeck and me on the ride back to Washington," Hamilton finished. We will then report to the Secretary."

"This might sound silly, but why don't I just report to Mr. Hull?"

"That's right, Mr. Stockton, it is silly." said Hamilton, allowing himself a little sarcasm. "You wait here until Hornbeck and I can talk with you. I'll send for you."

Hamilton walked the length of the Pullman car to where Dr. Stanley Hornbeck sat shuffling through piles of papers.

Hornbeck looked up at Hamilton. "That goddamned Roosevelt is going to ruin us," he said. "I swear to God he is a madman."

"For God's sake keep it down," Hamilton murmured. "The man *is* President." Three newspapermen who were traveling with Hull's party were talking to the Secretary in the middle of the car; other various secretaries, clerks, and technical experts were scattered around the car chatting and beginning to relax for the trip back to the capital. At the far end, Ben Stockton sat there staring out of the window. Hamilton quizzed Hornbeck. "What happened?" he asked.

Hornbeck glared. "That crippled sonovabitch thinks he knows so much about foreign policy. He threatened to send Harry Hopkins to Japan to work out a compromise."

Hamilton was startled. "He what? You mean he is really planning to meet with them. He has to be crazy."

Hornbeck snorted. "Of course he's crazy. More than that; he's dangerous. Do you realize that Hopkins might go over there and actually set up a meeting? I think Roosevelt would love that. He fancies himself as the personal savior of the entire world. I'm really getting sick of all this. That stupid show last month when he went up to meet

Churchill. Like a bunch of children, flitting around on their toy ships, it makes me sick."

"I'm getting slight vibrations from some of the Japan desk, Stanley. They're saying that there is no chance of peace."

Hornbeck always considered himself an intellectual, highly skilled at outguessing his opposite numbers. Somewhere in Tokyo his unknown alter ego was advising the Imperial government, and it was to this ethereal being that Hornbeck directed his thoughts. If his Japanese counterpart was anywhere as smart as he was, Hornbeck reasoned, there was no possibility of imminent war. The premise had been reasonable, the conclusions logical: The Japanese could not dream of conquering the United States in light of the current world situation. He said to Hamilton, "You'd better stifle such stupid considerations, Max. You've got to impress on your staff that we know how to handle this. Keep them in check and direct their opinions where they will do the most good. You know how to handle this, I'm sure."

Maxwell Hamilton was not at all sure that he could really control all of the men on his Japan desk; several of them were strong willed and had recently returned from Japan, where, not surprisingly, they had become somewhat disenchanted with Joe Grew. Personally, Hamilton had a close identification with Grew because both of them were men with long experience in the ways of the Department and neither could tolerate challenges that conflicted with traditional practices. But he would try.

"What was all that shouting when we were boarding?" Hornbeck asked.

Hamilton indicated the other end of the car. "One of Welles' 'brigands' " he said. He's just gotten back from spying on Grew to get a reaction to the Roosevelt-Churchill meeting. He's a pain in the neck."

Hornbeck considered that a while. "Well," he said judiciously, "get him blocked off. If I know any of Welles' bunch, he'll have some bad things to report about the reaction and that is one thing we do not need. Take care of that, too."

While the car they were in was being switched onto a Pennsylvania Railroad train bound for Washington, Hamilton went back and cornered Ben Stockton. By the time the train reached Philadelphia, Ben was ready to resign from the Department of State.

CHAPTER 10

WASHINGTON, D.C.

SEPTEMBER 13, 1941

From the second floor window of the War-State-Navy Building across from the White House, Ben Stockton could gaze down on the trees turning brown. The day was dismally overcast. Ben winced again as the booming voice of Maxwell Hamilton roared out of the office next door.

"You stupid, insignificant bastards don't know what you've done. I demand that you retract this."

There had been tension all morning on the second floor. Secretaries had moved quietly about their sundry tasks, conversations were hushed, there was a general air of subdued hysteria. The world was in a mess and wasn't getting any better. Diplomatic tempers flared in direct proportion to the severity of each new crisis. The mood that day was particularly ominous. Stockton found out why: Several members of the Far East Division had taken their courage in both hands and committed the capital crime—they had challenged Hornbeck and Hamilton on their handling of Japanese and American negotiations.

The chosen instrument of challenge was a memo, the contents of which was soon broadcast throughout the second floor.

DEPARTMENT OF STATE

Division of Far Eastern Affairs

September 13, 1941

MMH

The attached paper, drafted in the first instance by me and expanded after discussion with others, contains views which are entertained by Jones, Schuler, Davies, Tenney, Fales and me. We feel that the presentation of these views to the higher officers of the Department is of some importance, and we would, if it is possible, appreciate your sending forward the paper, with of course any covering comments which you might deem necessary.

September 13, 1941

It is reported in the press that there is about to be concluded an accord between the United States and Japan embodying an understanding on important questions of international relations.

Without knowing whether any such accord is in fact contemplated, certain officers of the Division of Far Eastern Affairs wish to place on record their view that it would be undesirable for the United States to enter into any accord with Japan which would tend either (1) to weaken Chinese resistance to Japan or (2) to relieve Japan from her present difficulties and thereby give her opportunity to gather her strength. Those officers entertain the view that the proposed accord as reported in the press, or any accord which does not provide for an immediate cessation of hostilities in China and effective guarantees for the early evacuation of China by Japanese armed forces, would constitute a betrayal of China which would undermine our position in China for many decades, would likely cause a surge of anti-American feeling throughout China and southeastern Asia, would seriously weaken throughout the world and in the United States the morale of those fighting and opposing aggression, and would be ineffective in achieving the end which presumably it would be designed to achieve, namely the protection of our Pacific flank while we turn our attention to the Atlantic. Those officers are of the belief that the Japanese Government is not in position to agree to the evacuation of China by Japanese armed forces; that any guarantees which might be given by the Japanese Government in this regard or in regard to further expansion southward, short of immediate withdrawal of troops, would not be effective as a real protection of our interests; that any accord at the present time would constitute an attempt at appeasement, with all of the current implications of the term, and would, with costly consequences, fail.

It wasn't an especially dynamic memo, but the words had been chosen carefully and the implication was there, as strong as anything that circulated around the Department of State at that time: The bosses were goofing up.

Stockton heard a voice that sounded like Frank Schuler's ask, "Will you pass it on up to the Secretary?" Ben was pretty sure it was Frank, but it was hard to tell since Hamilton was still booming: "No, dammit, you men are fools. You, Schuler, are the worst. You've been meddling ever since you came back. Like you did with those goddamned groceries. . . ."

Ben knew now it was Schuler on the receiving end of Hamilton's diatribe. The "Grocery Incident," as the old Japan hands in the Far Eastern Division called it, concerned the Japanese liner *Tatsuta Maru*. The U.S. Embassy in Tokyo had sent an order for several thousand dollar's worth of groceries to the United Grocery Company in San Francisco, but thanks to the embargo on shipments to Japan, the groceries had been delayed. The *Tatsuta Maru* was to be the last Japanese ship to sail from the U.S. mainland. In the corridors of State a great debate raged over how to get the groceries to Tokyo. Hamilton had contended that the "delicate" negotiations being conducted with the Japanese substantially prevented the Americans asking them to ferry groceries. Begging favors was unthinkable under the circumstances. As an old Tokyo hand, Frank Schuler appreciated the importance of provisions: If things got any worse—and Frank was sure they would—the Embassy personnel would have to get by on what they had. Secretary Hull predictably sided with Hamilton. As the days passed, the groceries grew in Hamilton's mind from a minor irritation to a diplomatic crisis of major proportions. The Far Eastern Division was close to paralysis.

But all of that changed. One weekend, Hamilton was away at Hot Springs with Secretary Hull and Schuler was Japanese duty officer in the Division. On that Saturday morning, another cable came from the Embassy in Tokyo: "WHERE ARE THE GROCERIES?" Schuler drafted a memorandum and submitted it to George Atcheson who was acting in Hamilton's absence. It passed to Undersecretary Sumner Welles who in turn was acting for Hull. The memo requested authority to apply to the Japanese Embassy in Washington for the *Tatsuta Maru* to carry the supplies. Welles approved without demur and the Japanese consented. It was that simple. The crisis was over. The Embassy would not, for the time being, run out of breakfast cereal or canned tuna fish.

But Hamilton did not see it that way. Monday morning all hell broke loose. Hamilton stormed into Schuler's office, his face livid. "Schuler, you've ruined everything! You've destroyed our

107

relations with Japan!" It took three weeks before he would again acknowledge Schuler as a member of the human race, let alone the State Department.

Now Schuler was back in the doghouse. Ben heard Hamilton continue his attack on Frank and then go after each man individually. But the six would not reconsider their opinions; they wanted the memo sent on up through channels.

Hamilton finally closed the meeting by saying, "I will consider your request. I will let you know what I decide, but you can be sure that the attitude you have displayed will be carefully noted in regard to your careers."

Ben Stockton was startled. Hamilton had made no effort to lower his voice. The offices in the building were closed off only by half doors with louvers—the kind seen back in the old Wild West saloons. Sound carried easily out into the hallways. Hamilton had just threatened career officers in public. Ben wondered how many others had heard the threat. He heard Cabot Coville, another old Japan hand, voice dissent, to which Hamilton responded, "I won't have this. I won't have my position questioned by junior officers."

Hamilton's ill-temper was well known; he had a reputation for driving his personal secretaries either to nervous breakdowns or resignation. But going after career men might be going too far.

Hamilton noisily dismissed the group. They scattered out into the halls and disappeared. Stockton started out of his office to find Frank Schuler, but as he walked down the hall, a yell came from Hamilton's office: "Stockton! Get in here!"

After overhearing Hamilton's tirade, Ben was prepared for almost anything, but he was not prepared for Hamilton saying: "Morning, Ben. How are things going?"

Hamilton was unpredictable. But now he was behaving so irrationally that it was becoming a cause for concern. Colleagues suspected him of collapsing under the strain; Stockton was inclined to agree. Hamilton just could not handle the pace of events.

They sat and chatted for a couple of minutes before Hamilton said, "I liked your report. So did Dr. Hornbeck."

Stockton sought to hide his confusion. On the train trip back to Washington from Hyde Park, both Hamilton and Hornbeck took issue with nearly every item he reported. The only exceptions had been the rare correspondences between Ambassador Grew's analysis of the Japanese situation and his own. "I thought you didn't like it?" Ben said.

Hamilton tried charm. "Look, Ben, we all have our own points of view, but, coupled with the weighted observations of Ambassador Grew, your report was quite satisfactory."

"Weighted?" Ben asked.

Hamilton extended his grin. "Certainly. You know how much experience Grew has with the Japanese. We would naturally weigh his opinions in with yours. I did that when I made the few changes that we felt were necessary."

"Changes?"

"Nothing of substance. Perfectly normal."

"I'd like to see the report as you corrected it." Ben said.

Hamilton was noncommittal. "In due course. We have another important project for you."

Dr. Hornbeck, it seemed, had been asked to give a broad, detailed position paper to Secretary

Hull and Stockton was to be drafted to serve as one of the source coordinators. He sensed that he was being conveniently pocketed out of any area of activity. Doing source research for a major paper could involve weeks of exhausting work, going through despatches and telegrams and over possibly years of files.

"We've pretty well established that the situation with Japan is stable and we need to support that," Hamilton said.

Stockton's eyes widened with amazement. "How can you call it stable? It's one of the biggest messes I've ever heard of."

Hamilton's grin switched to a frown. "I had hoped, what with you just back from there, that you would see the situation clearly. As Dr. Hornbeck has said, it is obvious that the Japanese government does not desire or intend or expect to have armed conflict with us. They are planning to bring China to her knees and then will have to spend a long time getting their own economic and political situation under control. Ambassador Grew confirms that the Japanese have rising hopes for peace and that many of their leaders want to listen to reason. It is only a small segment of militarists who keep causing the trouble."

"And what do you want from me?" Stockton asked, not bothering to conceal his animosity.

"As I said," Hamilton replied, "We need your views. You are the most recent visitor to Japan now in the Division. Your views are valuable."

"Mr. Hamilton," Stockton said, "I don't want to disappoint you; but I'm afraid I don't really subscribe to the views you just mentioned. I don't think the Japanese are ready to bring China to her knees. If anything, I think they'd just love to get the hell out of there."

Hamilton bristled. "Then why don't they? We have asked them dozens of times over the past few months."

"I think we're making a misstatement to them. They think we want them to pull all their forces off the mainland. As I understand our position, all we want is for them to halt their aggression against Chiang Kai-shek."

"That is correct."

"Well, sir, they think we're demanding their total withdrawal from Manchuria and maybe even Korea. They couldn't do that without a tremendous loss of face, and the Japanese just can't handle what they call loss of face. *Haji*—shame—is a profound emotion in Japan and. . . ."

Hamilton cut him off. "You don't have to give me a lecture. Of course we know they can't pull out of Manchuria. We don't want that. All we have asked for is a stop to their aggression."

"Then why don't we say that? Why don't we tell them they can hold on to Manchuria? Hell, Mr. Hamilton, they'd love to get out of China. It's costing them millions of dollars a day just to hold their own. They're certainly not winning."

"We have told them," said Hamilton, his voice rising once more. "Surely they *know* we don't mean for them to leave Manchuria?"

"I don't think so," Stockton said.

Hamilton began to fidget. "They know. I'm sure of that. It would only confuse matters."

Hamilton was fighting to keep himself under control. He had been ordered by Hornbeck to calm the Division. Now, with Coville, Schuler, and the other four screwing up the works with their stupid memo, it was vital for Stockton at least to be isolated. He spoke calmly. "I'll take your comments to Dr. Hornbeck. We will see what he says. Is that what you want?"

"I only want to do all I can for the Department. I am supposed to be working for Mr. Welles."

Hamilton was ill at ease. "Yes, well, there have been a few changes. You have been assigned to the position-paper project."

The deal had been worked out between Hull, Hornbeck, and Welles. Over the protest of Welles but with the blessings of Secretary Hull, Stockton and the other members of Welles' cadre were being assigned to various "pressing matters." The Secretary had stated in his mild but positive manner: "I don't care what gets done or who does it. The President wants and needs answers. I don't blame him. He is getting strong pressures from Marshall in the Army and he has to give them guidance or, before we know it, our own military will be jumping us into another Great War. Hornbeck; get me that report on Japan. Now."

Events had worked in favor of Hornbeck's plan for controlling the destiny of the nation. Using Grew in Tokyo and Hamilton in Washington, he would personally ensure peace between Japan and the United States. In his paper, a detailed and lengthy message for orientation of the President, Hornbeck would eventually state, without reservations, that it was impossible to conceive of a Japanese attack in December, that it was improbable there would be war in January or February, and that there was only half a chance that a war would ensue by March. The United States would have plenty of time to make its forces ready for a conflict, if there was to be a conflict.

CHAPTER 11

TOKYO, JAPAN

DECEMBER 2, 1941

Admiral Isoroku Yamamoto sat at the conference table in the meeting room next to his office on the third floor of the Imperial Navy Headquarters. The brown folder spread on the green baise tablecloth was crammed full; it held a current history of his battle to execute his own creation: Plan Z—the scheme to attack the U.S. Navy's Pacific Fleet at anchor in Pearl Harbor.

It was all there in the file.

He had won his fight against his conservative superiors who saw the attack as an impossible gamble. He continued efforts to instill some enthusiasm in the men who doubted the possibility of success. One of the doubters was the commander of Yamamoto's precious Carrier Fleet which even now was steaming eastward in the northern Pacific.

A few days before, he had boarded the flagship *Akagi* and said to his ship commanders, "I expect this operation to be a success." Traditionally, commanders-in-chief in the Japanese Navy only *hoped* for success; Yamamoto's departure from ritual displayed his confidence. He *expected* success. Yamamoto had been toasted with *ban-*

zais for the Emperor; he had left his commanders believing in victory.

Yamamoto was a dedicated bridge player. Over the past several months, he had used every trick he had learned during his long years in the Imperial Navy, and every trick he had picked up at the bridge table. He had tried every ploy from threatening to resign to declaring that he would personally accompany the attack fleet. He had won and now his Carrier Fleet was en route.

At the end of the room, a junior officer wearing the insignia of an Admiral's aide stood at attention, his eyes riveted to the wall opposite.

In a quiet voice, Yamamoto called the aide who approached silently. "It is a miserable afternoon," the Admiral said.

"Hai," the aide snapped back. The misty, chilly weather outside was not important, but if the Admiral wanted to talk about the weather, the aide was not about to question such a great man.

"We are at a memorable moment for our Navy and our Empire," said Yamamoto.

"Hai," the aide snapped again. Everyone in headquarters knew what was happening; the excitement of the event had gripped each man's imagination. From the mainland constant prayers silently followed the warriors out to sea.

Yamamoto looked down at the folder and picked up one of the pieces of paper near the bottom of the pile. It had been prepared weeks before; carefully written, no copies made, only Yamamoto carried the document around with him. He studied the words, repeated them silently to himself over and over again. Then he read aloud the final words necessary to implement Operational Order One of Plan Z: *"Niitaka-Yama Nobore"*—"Climb Mount Niitaka"

114

The young aide felt his head reel and his knees go weak with excitement; the words had been spoken.

Yamamoto handed the paper to the aide and said, "Send this out. Now."

The moment was too great for the aide. Casting aside any thoughts of proper, disciplined behavior, he blurted out, "Admiral, you give me great honor in this duty."

The Admiral smiled and looked up at his aide. He used his friendliest, warmest voice to say, "Remember this moment. If it succeeds then you may tell your grandchildren. If it fails then there will be no grandchildren." The aide beamed with pride and confidence, then Yamamoto said, "Go now. Our Fleet waits for those words."

Alone, the Admiral went to the window and looked out over Tokyo. He was not affected by the dismal afternoon; any December afternoon at 5:30 could be miserable in Tokyo. Not even the weather could be a bad omen. Not for this event. Every fiber of his mind and body had strained to ensure the success of Plan Z. The intelligence gathering had been brilliant. His brazen plan to send spies right into the enemy's base had paid off. Daily reports were coming back from the Japanese Consulate in Honolulu; precise reports on every ship's dockage or anchorage. The training of the aircraft crews had been magnificent. The Admiral himself had selected the training location, and with many hard weeks of training behind them, the pilots knew their job inside out. They would not fail. The politicians had done their jobs well; and the Ambassador he had sent abroad to lie for his country. The politicians and the diplomats had not failed.

Yamamoto had personally timed the attack.

Navy meteorologists had recommended December 8 because of the favorable phase of the moon. Yamamoto knew better. His years at Harvard and his tours of duty as a Naval attaché had told him that Sunday would be perfect. The peace-time U.S. Navy set aside Saturday night for relaxation and Sunday for rest. Yamamoto's forces would blast that peaceful repose.

In five days, his plan would be put to the test. He would know then if he had overbid his grand slam.

FACTUM

0615 am	7 Dec 1941	First wave of attack planes takes off.
0759 am	7 Dec 1941	Rear Admiral Patrick Bellinger at his headquarters on Ford Island sounds alarm: "Air raid. Pearl Harbor. This is no drill."
0945 am	7 Dec 1941	Second and final wave of attacking Japanese aircraft break off attack.

U.S. LOSSES:

Battleship *Arizona*—Total Loss
Battleship *Oklahoma*—Total Loss
Battleship *California*—Severe Damage
Battleship *West Virginia*—Severe Damage

Battleship *Utah*—Sunk
Cruiser *Helena*—Severe Damage
Cruiser *Honolulu*—Severe Damage
Cruiser *Raleigh*—Severe Damage
Destroyer *Downes*—Total Loss
Destroyer *Cassin*—Total Loss
Minelayer *Ogala*—Sunk

Army Air Corps aircraft: 96 destroyed, 128 damaged
Navy Fleet aircraft: 92 destroyed, 31 damaged

Personnel Casualties:
  Army: 218 killed; 364 wounded
  Navy: 2008 killed; 710 wounded
  Marines: 109 killed; 69 wounded

JAPANESE LOSSES:
  Attack Aircraft: 29 shot down or crashed
  Fleet ships: NONE LOST
  Personnel Casualties: 185 killed in action

1305 pm   26 Dec 1941   Task Force returns safely to Japan.

Part Two

CHAPTER 12

TOKYO, JAPAN

JANUARY 19, 1942

Ambassador Grew left the small sitting room in the official residence of the Embassy: he would not be long, he said. Mme. Gorge and Alice Grew were having tea. In Grew's private office, he and the Swiss Minister, Camille Gorge, got quickly to the business at hand.

The Swiss had been assigned to act for the United States in matters of protocol for the duration of hostilities. Gorge had his work cut out for him in arranging the exchange of American Embassy staff for the Japanese Embassy personnel trapped in the States by the outbreak of war.

In violation of protocol, Gorge was also transmitting communications from Washington to Grew. There was nothing of a strategic nature in the messages the Swiss Minister smuggled into the American Embassy. There was nothing sensational which Washington wished to transmit to Grew for the simple reason that the corridors of power there were buzzing with far more critical issues than his safety or comfort. There was a war on in the Pacific, and Hitler had joined his

Japanese Axis ally in a declaration of war on the United States. Joe Grew loomed pretty small in the context.

"Not much," Gorge announced as he opened his briefcase. "Only one large envelope."

Grew accepted it graciously. "A drink?" he offered. "How about a Napoleon?"

"It is very early." Then, with Gallic charm, he overcame his reluctance. "But, why not? I would enjoy that very much."

Grew poured two stiff brandies. "We might as well drink it up," he said. "The Japs are going to force us to sell everything and the proceeds will be frozen. It is nothing but highway robbery. Surely not in the spirit of normal international usage."

Grew had been harping about "normal international usage" ever since word first came that war had been declared. It violated his sensibilities to think that the Japanese would not play by the rules of international diplomacy; the war be damned, protocol demanded. . . .

"What can I say?" Gorge shrugged. "These are difficult times."

Grew had an Embassy to dispose of for the duration. The Swiss would see to the maintenance of the buildings and they would do their best to prevent any damage. "No," Gorge said, "no Swiss would move in, that would be compromising. We will merely continue to use the Japanese staff you have employed now. Will that be satisfactory?"

Grew spent a half-hour on the papers in the sealed packet while Gorge saw to it that as little as possible of the brandy was wasted. There was nothing of significance except one personal envelope which Grew would open only when he was alone. The address was scrawled in Hornbeck's handwriting.

"There is nothing demanding an immediate reply," said Grew. "I have only this to go out. If you could possibly see to it I'd really. . . ."

The Swiss Minister cut Grew off; the less said about their clandestine mail service the better. He took the outgoing packet and placed it in his case. They were on their fifth brandy when Gorge brought out a small, folded piece of newsprint. Sliding it across the high polish of Grew's desk, he said, "I cut this out of the *International Herald-Tribune* from Paris. I thought you might like to see it."

Grew picked up the article and began to read it. His skin went red, and his tic began its familiar dance.

December 15, 1941

WASHINGTON DAILY MERRY-GO-ROUND

by Drew Pearson and Robert S. Allen

It is now possible to tell the tragic inside story of the diplomatic negotiations which Secretary Hull was conducting while the Japanese were preparing their secret attack on Pearl Harbor and the United States.

The real story goes back to early August when Prince Konoye sent a cable to the President asking that they meet at a conference to discuss Pacific problems. When this was received in the State Department, Maxwell Hamilton, chief of the department's Far Eastern Division proposed that the United States negotiate.

However, a group of his advisors in the Far Eastern Division, who had been in Japan recently, were convinced that everything Japan was doing pointed to war against the United States. They were convinced that any Japanese diplomatic negotiations were a mere bluff for the purpose of consuming time while Japan finished preparations.

This group was not consulted, however, regarding conversations. So finally they drafted a two-page memorandum warning that diplomatic negotiations would lead to disaster. Also they wanted to go over Max Hamilton's head to Secretary Hull.

Those who signed this warning were *Cabot Coville, Joseph M. Jones, Frank A. Schuler, John P. Davies, Herbert Fales and E. Paul Tenney.*

* * *

Immediately they were summoned before Hamilton, the Chief of the Far Eastern Division.

Hamilton bawled out his subordinates and told them they had no business interfering. But they insisted that their memorandum be taken direct to Secretary Hull. And Cabot Coville resigned. When his resignation came to the attention of Assistant Secretary Berle, however, Berle refused to accept it and *Coville was transferred to the Philippines, where he is today. The chief results of his*

*efforts are that today he is being subjected
to the bombing attacks which he himself,
warned were coming.*

These men were all hardened experts on
the Far East who had lived there and who
knew Japan. They were not youngsters.
However, their warning memorandum,
though it finally reached the hands of Secretary Hull, made no impression. A few weeks
later special envoy Kurusu was sent to
Washington with a big blare of Tokyo
trumpets about peace and the negotiations
continued.

"Who?" he said, "Who could believe such
drivel?"

"Mr. Drew Pearson, I think," said the undiplo-
matic Swiss. It was time to rejoin the ladies.

Grew's wife, Alice, was telling a funny story
about the Embassy's new, private golf course.

"What?" the Swiss Minister asked in a shocked
tone of voice.

Grew beamed broadly. "Didn't I mention it?
Within a week of those Japs closing us inside, my
boys got together and turned the parking lot and
grounds into quite an admirable course. Nine
holes, 422 yards, even water hazards in the fish
ponds. Quite nice, really. I made my first hole-in-
one the other day. I'd ask you to play, but I'm
afraid it might upset the War Lords down at the
prefecture of police."

The Swiss Minister broke out laughing. "I
must salute you. Your nation is at war, there
seems to be no indication of when—or if—you
will be repatriated, and the Japanese quite possibly could come in here and slaughter all of you.
Marvelous."

Grew's chest puffed. He crossed the room and stood by Alice. "We're from good stock, you know." He treated Gorge to a recital of the family history, with copious mention of Commodore Perry. Gorge listened politely; he had heard the story no more than half a dozen times before. An interjection from Mrs. Grew gave him a chance to make his excuses and leave; he was dreading the possibility of hearing Grew's rendition of the time he shot a tiger in India. Around diplomatic circles, the tiger shoot was frequently referred to as Grew's most notable qualification for an ambassadorial post in Asia.

Grew and his wife did not see their guests out of the Embassy; there was a possibility that the Japanese guard on the front gate would not unlatch the handle, thus forcing Grew into the undignified position of having to open the door himself.

As soon as the Swiss were gone, Grew summoned Eugene Dooman to his private office.

Dooman was a Japanese-born career Foreign Service Officer. He had attended Trinity College and was appointed as student interpreter in Japan in 1912. He was the child of naturalized Syrian parents and possessed of a massive and unjustified paranoia about his background. But he could speak, read, and even write the complex language of 23,000 characters. Like Grew, Dooman had been one of the strongest proponents of the bogus peace negotiations. He was far from stupid and well-versed in Sino-Japanese history, but as inclined to blind optimism as his boss. Dooman had spent little time in the United States and was consequently incapable of accurately conveying the true spirit of America to his

Japanese counterparts. Things might otherwise have turned out differently.

But Grew needed Dooman. The Ambassador knew no Japanese. That, in itself, was not unusual in the Foreign Service of that day, but it did not help Grew keep track of his subordinate's dealings with the Japanese. Dooman, it was whispered, went in for wife-swapping. The Ambassador took care to keep himself ignorant of that activity.

Of all the personnel in the U.S. Embassy, Dooman was the most trusted and loyal. Mack Priest had been rotated back to Washington before the attack, but Priest was only a lackey; Dooman was a cohort.

Dooman arrived in Grew's office in a rumpled suit. Fastidious in his own dress, Grew knew there was little he could do to change Dooman's slovenly appearance; it was a nasty wart that had to be lived with. The Japanese had cut off laundry facilities in any case, so there was little point chiding Dooman for his sartorial lapses.

As Dooman sat down, Grew slid the newspaper article across the desk. Dooman read it, contemplated it, and gave his considered judgment: "Schuler! Coville! What the hell do they know? I told you that damned Schuler was a meddler, and Coville, when was he here? Back in '38 and '39. . . ."

"He came in '36," Grew interjected.

"No matter. The snotty little shit. Schuler and Coville, shit!"

"That paper makes them look pretty good," the Ambassador pointed out.

Dooman's anger boiled over again. "Those bastards sitting on their fat butts back there! Dammit, Joe, I'll burn their asses."

Grew winced, not so much at the obscenities as the use of his given name. Living together in cramped quarters might be unavoidable, but it did not and could not be allowed to permit that sort of gross overfamiliarity. All of the officers, staff, and their families had gathered inside the Embassy compound. The Japanese did not want their citizens assaulting American diplomatic staff, as well they might have, being under the impression that their country's genuine quest for peace had been frustrated by American intransigence. The end result was that the Americans were living in very close quarters. Magnanimously, Grew invited even low-level staff people to his table in strict rotation, but it could not be said that he was enjoying the experience.

"I think Coville and Schuler and the others will be adequately taken care of by our friends in Washington," he told Dooman. "The reason I wanted you to see that was because it has profound implications, especially when considered with this." He handed Dooman the personal note from Dr. Stanley Hornbeck.

Dec. 20, 1941

Dear Joe,

Hope all is going well for you in this difficult time. All of us in the Department are working to get you returned.

I feel you and I are of kindred spirits knowing that we did all we could to halt this horrible turn of events. It would be nice to say that our mutual efforts are being acknowledged, but I must report that some forces are at work to the contrary. The President has commissioned Justice Roberts

126

to investigate the events leading up to the war; no one yet knows just what course the inquiry will take. In anticipation of your return, I feel it might be wise for you to prepare yourself to aid in any investigation which might be conducted upon your return. Some factions are suggesting that we did not do all that was possible to prevent the war; I disagree violently with them. I am sure you will be handsomely prepared by the time you return and your friends here will do everything necessary to support you.

I know you will bear up under this trial in the manner with which you have always handled adversity.

Fondly,
SKH

Dooman did not lack brains. He read the Hornbeck note again, thought it over, and said, "Hornbeck is saying something important in this, Joe."

"Of course he is," said the Ambassador.

"I mean there is something here that he could not come out and state clearly."

Grew's brows furrowed.

Dooman read the message again, then said, "He's giving us a warning."

Grew dismissed the idea. "Now, Dooman, don't be silly. Doctor Hornbeck is a gentleman of the first order."

"I saw him last summer," Dooman replied. "He is on the ball. We agreed entirely that the peace faction would be able to counter the militarists, but. . . ."

"Yes," said Grew. "He has always relied on our assessments. I consider him one of the most outstanding men who has ever headed the Far Eastern Division. He has collected great talent around him in Hamilton and Ballantine; we had no way of knowing the militarists would act with such treachery."

Dooman tried again. "The crux of this note," he said deliberately, "is his phrase: *it might be wise for you to prepare yourself*. That's the meat of it."

"I will certainly be prepared," Grew said. I have my diaries; we have copies of all the despatches and telegrams. We will be fully prepared."

"And what will your diaries and despatches show?"

"They will show all of the work and energy we put into doing our job. No one could fault that."

Dooman lurched up out of his seat and walked to the window looking out into the garden. Off to the right, he could see the Japanese police guards on duty. In the parking lot two couples were passing the time at badminton.

"I wish we knew what the hell was going on in Washington," the Counselor said. "We are in such a vacuum here."

Within hours of the attack on Pearl Harbor the Japanese authorities had closed off the Embassy compound. In a nine-point statement, the position of the Embassy personnel was laid down: They were virtual prisoners. While granting undefined rights in accordance with "customary international usages," telephone and telegraph facilities were cut off and all radios confiscated. The only sources of communications or information were diplomatic intercourse with the Swiss and the odd Japanese-language newspaper that found its way into the compound. The diplomatic dialogue was limited to only the most official language, except in cases of personal, compassionate need. The Japanese kept a very close check on the meetings. Their Japanese newspapers were full of war propaganda. The internees had little access to accurate news.

Grew looked carefully at his antique gold watch. He always made a ceremony of finding out the time. "We must go to tea, Dooman," he announced. "Alice is going to play for us."

Dooman spun from the window. "Joe, we've got a problem," he said forcefully. "Damn it, tea can wait."

But tea could not wait. Grew stood, snapping the watchcover shut and replacing it in the security of his vest pocket. "We must not be late," he pronounced.

As Dooman passed the desk, he reached down, grabbed the note from Dr. Hornbeck, and jammed it into his pocket. "Why?" Grew asked.

"I want to read it again."

When the tiny Embassy golf course had been established by the men of the staff, the women had turned the Community Room in the Chancery into a meeting place. It became known as "The Lido." It was comfortable enough. There was a cozy fireplace and plenty of room for bridge games, mah-jongg, chess, and, when possible, entertainment. Grew had vetoed anything as overt as dancing, on the grounds that the Japanese might see it as frivolous, but music was permitted either from the piano or the record player. Grew's wife, Alice, played mother hen to most of the activities.

Tea had been served. Alice played, and the Ambassador volunteered a couple of ancient show tunes himself. "We must keep up morale, you know," he reminded Dooman. The twelve members of the staff who had been allowed to attend the tea were milling about, waiting politely so that they could launch games of bridge or chess.

Alone with Grew in front of the fireplace, Dooman smiled his understanding. "Hornbeck wants us to check any written matter we have. I'm sure that's what he was trying to say in his note."

Grew lit a cigar. "I don't understand?"

Dooman looked about furtively. "Look. Tie in that article of Drew Pearson's with the note. There are some kind of hearings going on and it looks like there is a finger being pointed at the Department."

"Nonsense," said the Ambassador.

"May be," Dooman said, "maybe not. Pearson used one of his 'now-it-can-be-told' gimmicks. It could be that there is other talk."

"Pearson is *always* sounding mysterious," said Grew. "Why would he have anything against what State has done?"

"Look, the article takes a pretty good swipe at Hamilton. That means Hornbeck, too."

"Pearson had been against Dr. Hornbeck for years," Grew observed.

"Okay," Dooman pressed on. "And Hornbeck sends you a warning. . . ."

"That is your assumption," Grew cut in.

Dooman continued, "A warning to make sure that our records are not damaging. That's it, so that there is nothing that could point a finger at us."

Grew was getting impatient. "Dooman, the record speaks for itself. It is all there in our despatches and my diaries."

Dooman waited for a moment before he spoke.

He was not sure Grew would take kindly to the warning he felt compelled to deliver. "I think Hornbeck was saying that maybe the record should not be allowed to speak for itself."

Drew's face froze. "Dooman," he said, with all the considerable pomposity he could muster, "I think you are not reading this whole thing properly. Our record is cast in bronze. Let it stand."

"It is *not* cast in bronze," said Dooman. "It is written on paper."

"Do I understand you correctly?" the Ambassador asked. "Do I take it that it is your considered opinion that Dr. Hornbeck is suggesting that we might be in trouble for what we have done? That one of the top policy men in our Department is trying to warn us that history will prove that we were derelict in our duty? Am I correct?"

Dooman weighed the situation. Long ago he had latched his hopes for a diplomatic career on Joe Grew. He had even cut off valuable Japanese Army liaisons because Grew had felt it was not productive to associate with people of such small influence. To Dooman's mind his whole future was riding on this man standing in front of him; if Grew fell from grace, so would Dooman. "I think," said Dooman, weighing his words carefully, "that your place in history might be marred by misunderstanding."

"Why?" wailed Grew. "Why? And *how*, in God's name?"

Dooman had already worked that one out. With Drew Pearson dropping hints and with a Presidential inquiry in the offing, it looked very much to him as if somebody was looking for someone to blame for the war. It was a pretty good guess that the collective culprit might end up being the Department of State.

His view was not welcome to Grew. The thought was inconceivable to him; people must know that he was a great peacemaker. He could not deny that he had failed to prevent war, in spite of his multifarious diplomatic skills. But could he truly be blamed for it?

"Surely," Grew said in a subdued voice, "no one can say we did not do our job well."

"Someone," said Dooman gently, "might say the Department failed and that could lead to someone saying the Ambassador to Japan failed. It is possible."

Grew's head shook in protest. "No," he insisted. "We filed long and detailed analyses of the situation. Nothing went unreported. I am very proud of all that we did."

Henri Smith-Hutton, the unemployed Naval Attaché, interrupted to ask if a golf tournament could be staged the next day. Grew snapped himself out of his concentration and gave his blessings. After a few good-natured remarks with the Navy Lieutenant Commander, Grew said that he and Dooman had some business to go over before cocktails. They left the Community Room and went back to his office.

By the time they were alone again, Grew had digested Dooman's concept. He spoke first as they took their chairs. "I can think of ten items we passed on that show we were doing all we could."

"Like the Schreiber report?" Dooman suggested.

Pearl Harbor. Of course. Grew remembered quite well the Peruvian Minister's warning. "But we sent that," he said in triumph. "It went out by both telegram and despatch."

"But," Dooman asked, "do you remember the wording?"

"Of course."

"Then don't you think that someone might say we were wrong, negligent, and culpable for discounting the tip by saying we gave no credence to it?"

"That was your idea," said Grew. "You said Schreiber was not all that reliable."

"Right," Dooman admitted. "But you agreed. You did not have all that much respect for him in the first place. You felt it was a good idea to qualify the report so that we could not be considered rumor-mongers. The despatch went over your signature. The questions will be asked of you."

Grew began to feel nervous. "But surely we are not here to be common spies? Anyone would understand that it was virtually impossible for us to gain any reliable information because the Japanese were being so strict on security."

"That's just the point, Joe. We had a piece of intelligence and we watered it down. I still think it was probably a lucky guess on Schreiber's part, but the damned thing is there. He called the shot and we gave no credence to it. If there is any concerted effort going on to nail somebody for the outbreak of war, then they will surely grab hold of that with both hands."

Grew's hands were beginning to sweat. He was embarrassed because he felt it was a sign of weakness. "But," he argued, "that is only one small item."

"Sure," said Dooman. "And what about Konoye? What about Tojo? What about Kurusu?"

Grew saw now the black portrait that could be painted. Prince Konoye had been one of his closest friends. It was obvious now that preparations had been underway for a long time, while the Prince had been Prime Minister, yet Grew had sent despatches praising Konoye's efforts for peace. And General Tojo. When he had been named Prime Minister, Grew had reported that Tojo would keep the militarists in check. As far as Kurusu was concerned, Grew had placed his blessings on his appointment as Special Ambassador to Washington. He had let the fox into the coop. Lumped together, possibly with other incriminating incidents, the whole thing could look rather bad. Then there was the matter of items which had not been passed on. The extraordinary war games that Admiral Yamamoto had held the previous summer. That had not been reported even though there had been a strong feeling around the Embassy that the games might include the attack on Pearl Harbor. Grew had not wanted to be thought of as crying wolf. He remembered another report that was never sent: Back on December 2, just a few days before the attack on Pearl Harbor, there had been a special meeting of the Imperial Council. There had been guesses, one of them Grew's, that the Japanese might be discussing war and the attack on Pearl Harbor. But, because negotiations were underway, Grew did not want to make it look as if the militarists were so strong that they could sway the Imperial Council. He had rejected that idea, but he did note it in his diary.

"My God," he said to Dooman, "My diary!"

Dooman sat back and relaxed. He had made his point.

Since his youth Grew had maintained a diary detailing his contribution to diplomacy. Never in any doubt about his positive contribution to the welfare of his country, he had allowed himself the luxury of considerable candor. After all, it was the stuff of history. He could remember recording the item about the Imperial Council meeting; he had even, he recalled, referred to the guess about an attack on Pearl Harbor. He had also noted that the climate in Tokyo was ideal for all sorts of unfounded rumors and that one was so far-fetched that he could not bring himself to commit it to an official communiqué.

But what would it look like to a person not privy to the situation at the time? Suppose some investigative committee began to study that diary; what else would they find that, on the surface, would appear to be damning?

His voice a whisper, Grew said, "It could look bad."

"Exactly," said Dooman.

The golf tournament had been rescheduled and was not complete on Thursday afternoon. The Ambassador had made it up one leg but was eliminated by his secretary. It was politely acknowledged that Grew had been distracted by the raucous noise of the badminton tournament which, in a masterstroke of bad planning, had been put on for the same afternoon. After awards ceremonies, thought by some to be "childish" and by others "morale-boosting," Grew hosted all of the contestants to drinks in the gardens. With everyone in good spirits, Grew made his excuses and left the gathering. Alice and most of the women were in the Community Room working hard at their bridge games, so he was not missed as he climbed to the second floor of the Embassy and entered the Code Room.

Grew had treated the mechanics of coding with

a certain disdain, but he had at least been into the Code Room from time to time. He found it shocking now to see the gaps where the code machines had been; they had been removed and destroyed. But the room was the most secure place in the Embassy, so it had been chosen by Dooman for his work. As Grew let himself in with one of the two keys (Dooman had the other), he heard hurried movement inside. With the door open, Grew immediately saw the cause: Miss Penelope Morton was in the room with Gene Dooman.

Miss Morton was not, by any standard, a ravishing beauty. Unkind persons had in fact claimed to detect a superficial facial resemblance to the horse family. But not much else was available within the compound. Suddenly her dormant charms were being discovered by interested males on the staff. Dooman, through all of his years of service, had built a reputation for consorting with various Japanese girls, and word was that he maintained a mistress from time to time. That he was slovenly and unkempt made him unattractive to some of the American women who might otherwise have enjoyed an affair with the Counselor of the Embassy, but apparently his appearance did not put off his Japanese girls. It seemed obvious to Grew that Miss Morton was not finding Dooman repugnant either; she was having an awful time straightening her skirt and tucking in her blouse.

"Eh, Dooman," Grew said in his heavy I-mean-business voice, "I'd like to talk to you."

Miss Morton was totally flustered. "Ah, Mr. Ambassador . . . ah, Joe . . . we were. . . ."

Smiling with syrupy politeness, Grew raised a pontifical hand and cut her off. "I'm sure Mr.

Dooman will excuse you, Miss Morton," he allowed.

"Sure . . . sure, Penny. You run along," said Dooman. "We'll get back to work later . . . okay?"

Miss Morton fled gratefully.

As the door closed, Dooman said, "We've made it up through October, 1940; it is a hell of a lot of work."

Sarcastically, Grew said, "It seems to me that you have also made it up through the lady's skirt."

Dooman broke into a broad grin. Since the internment his relationship with the Ambassador had been growing close and candid. Never before had Grew been so personally communicative, and in the good-natured atmosphere, Grew could almost be said to have been acting human with the staff members.

Dooman ignored the quip about Penny Morton. He was more interested in establishing the proper priority for his work. "There isn't really too much back in 1940. You kind of missed it on the signing of the Tripartite Pact when you reported that most of the Japs felt the pact was not important. And your message on the Emperor and Konoye being 'dead against' the agreement with Italy and Germany kind of missed the mark. But other than that there is nothing really damning."

Grew pulled a chair from under one of the paper-strewn desks and sat down. He lit a cigar, furrowed his brows, and massaged his forehead with his fingertips. He was fighting to remember the fall of 1940. After a couple of minutes, he said, "I could do a piece saying I had second thoughts on the Japanese reactions. That would work."

Dooman shook his head. "It would fall out of number sequence in the despatches."

"We could drop one of the other despatches."

"Maybe," Dooman replied, his tone hesitant.

"What about in the diary?"

Dooman nodded. "That would be best, I think."

Then Grew said, "There was a lot going on. Remember the 2,600-year celebration. Looking back, it all seems pretty ominous."

On the event of the celebration of the 2,600th year of the Japanese Empire, he had sent back glowing reports about the charm of the observance and how relations were looking good for Japan and the United States and how Admiral Nomura would be a great ambassador to Washington. He had missed completely the significance of one great gesture. The Emperor, for the first time in history, had joined a garden party of fifty thousand people and sat down to eat exactly the same food as everyone else in attendance. Now, with war underway, the implication of that gathering was clear to Grew: One Hundred Million People with One Mind. It had been the slogan of the war party come to life.

The work in the Code Room involved only Grew, Dooman, and Penny Morton. The men knew what they were up to, the woman cared only that she was serving, as she later described him, "the greatest Ambassador there has ever been." Grew had enticed her with implied promises of a bright future in the Department of State, and Dooman had romanced her physically. Penny Morton joined the plot gladly. She knew that Grew was well placed in Washington and Dooman was a damn sight better than the low-level military personnel whose attentions had mostly been confined to a quick grope and the odd lay under cover of darkness.

Some of the work had been easy, involving only making note of despatches sent to Washington and fabricating new verbiage that would change or lessen the force of Grew's disastrous advice. More difficult was the restructuring of telegrams which would have been sent in code over the normal communications routes. In order to maintain the integrity of the code system, the messages would have been paraphrased in Washington before being distributed. Grew and Dooman had to try to outguess the paraphrasers in Washington so that they could at least subsequently challenge the wording used on documents distributed around the Department.

Grew sought reassurance as he had done frequently since their efforts had been launched. "I hope you are right, Gene."

Dooman arched back in his swivel chair, locked his hands in back of his head, and said, "I am convinced. The more I think about it; the more positive I am: Hornbeck is looking out for our asses, Joe. And we can be grateful."

Dooman would not say it to Grew's face, but, since digging back through the chronological files, he had found that Grew's messages were consistent only in their ambiguity. The single positive thread through the reportage was that the Japanese peace faction would prevail in the end.

They played with words for another hour. Where they could not change a word to alter the meaning they would reconstruct a sentence. The work was demeaning for Grew. He had always felt his words should be preserved for posterity. But Dooman found the task invigorating. Not only was he doing a favor for certain members of the Foreign Service, he was also accumulating highly embarrassing data on Grew. And that could be both an insurance and a promise for the future.

Tired from the labors, Grew stood. "God," he sighed. "I do wish we could be gone from this place. If they would just see to our repatriation."

Things had been moving tediously. The Japanese government had vacillated on the matter of shipping the American diplomats and citizens out of Japan and several schedules had already been scrapped.

Dooman smiled. "Don't be in too much of a hurry. We have a lot of work to do."

Grew headed toward the door; cocktails would be served shortly. He chided Dooman. "Are you sure you aren't becoming fond of Miss Morton's charms?"

"No chance," said Dooman. "I can do better than that."

"Watch out for Crocker," said Grew, attempting some uncharacteristic banter. "I caught him moving his eye toward her at dinner the other night."

Dooman laughed back. "I'm not worried. Would you send her back if you see her, please?"

Grew said he would.

CHAPTER 13

WASHINGTON, D.C.

February 22, 1942

Diagonally across Lafayette Square from the Department of State building sat the staid old Cosmos Club. It was a watering hole for upper-echelon government officials and a quiet place for the elite of the diplomatic service to eat.

Since the outbreak of the war there had been a pronounced change of mood among the clusters of Department of State types who lunched at the club. Before Pearl Harbor they had had some sense of purpose; ever since they were morbid and apathetic when they were not irritable. Foreign policy was no longer in the hands of the striped trousers brigade from State: The will of the United States was expressed instead through the might of her armed forces. They did not relish their sudden redundancy.

One large round table by a window looking out onto H Street was reserved on a regular basis for Dr. Stanley Hornbeck and his entourage. His confidants called it the "Round Table." Despite his obvious failure as chief foreign policy advisor to the Secretary of State, Hornbeck continued holding court as if he possessed the answers to all the world's problems.

The military thought otherwise and did not

mind saying so. "You had your chance, now leave this to us professionals," one officer had contemptuously advised him. Hornbeck was furious. He had no intention of giving up any power or influence if he could avoid it.

On the day of the golf match at the Embassy in Tokyo, Hornbeck was presiding at his table. Attending were Maxwell Hamilton, Mack Priest, Joseph Ballantine, and Alger Hiss.

The gathering held an impressive array of titles for a small group. Hornbeck was a political advisor to the Secretary of State. Hamilton was Chief of the Far Eastern Division and Ballantine headed up the Japan desk as Assistant Chief. Priest had recently returned from Tokyo and Hiss was working as Hornbeck's assistant.

Hornbeck's lunches were not generally inordinately long, considering the conspicuous lack of furious activity in the Department. But only a few within the Department knew that these sessions had a serious and devious purpose.

Ballantine indicated what it was as coffee was served. "I just hope Grew got the message," he said.

"Maybe they'll be interned throughout the war," Hiss offered.

"There're a few shitheads I'd like to see stay over there," Priest contributed.

The others did not hide their disapproval of his language; exposure to the civilities of such places as the Cosmos Club had not improved Priest's manners all that much.

Ignoring both comments, Hornbeck spoke of Ballantine's hopes. "I can't imagine him missing the point. He has to know how heavy this all looks. My God, I based most of my November paper on some of his assessments."

"That fuckin' Drew Pearson did his number again on that one," said Priest. "How the hell'd he get it?"

Pearson had not stopped at a newspaper article. The Sunday evening before, on his weekly radio broadcast, he had leveled one of his famous broadsides at Hornbeck. In his usual, sensational manner, he had reported that ". . . on November 22, 1941, just fifteen days before Pearl Harbor, he [Hornbeck] wrote an important memorandum to the Secretary of State advising that Japan never would attack the United States."

There had been a frantic flurry at the Department the next morning, and Hornbeck appeared before the official Department recorder. Much energy was poured into pointing out that Pearson had been wrong in his facts. He was. The message had been written on November *27*, not on the 22nd as Pearson had claimed. Hornbeck might as well have kept quiet. The corrected version was even more damning because it indicated the memorandum came ten days, rather than the fifteen days Pearson mentioned, before the sneak attack. In his defense of himself, Hornbeck argued that he had made no such claim. He freely admitted that he had stated on September 3, 1941, that Japan would not attack the United States within the next three months, but he claimed to have said no such thing on November 27, 1941. There was considerable amusement in the Department when the true text became known there. Hornbeck had written:

In the opinion of the undersigned, the Japanese Government does not desire or intend or expect to

143

have forthwith armed conflict with the United States. The Japanese Government, while launching new offensive operations at some point or points in the Far East, will endeavor to avoid attacking or being attacked by the United States. It therefore will not order or encourage action by its agents (foremost among which are its armed forces) which, if taken, would lead toward use by the United States of armed force by way of retaliation or resistance. So far as relations directly between the United States and Japan are concerned there is less reason today than there was a year ago for the United States to be apprehensive lest Japan make "war" on this country. Stated briefly, the undersigned does not believe that this country is now on the immediate verge of "war" in the Pacific.
/signed/SKH/

"I'll have to stand the gaff on that one," Hornbeck admitted. "I'd like to know if Pearson has an actual copy or if he was only slipped a summary. It would be much easier to defend if he didn't have the actual document. But," he said as he sipped his coffee, "I'm on record with that; we've got to go forward."

Hamilton had remained silent through most of the lunch. He had little idea of what they were referring to as "moving forward" and he had no desire to learn. After the ignominious collapse of peace efforts, he wanted as little as possible to do with Japan. He had wrangled himself a post in the Moscow Embassy as far away from Washington and the shame of Pearl Harbor as he could get. He knew that something was going on because of Hornbeck, Ballantine and Priest's conversation but had no desire to get involved. He would have liked to cover his ears; he felt an overpowering urge to shut them up. But he held his peace and tried to redirect the conversation to a more comfortable area.

"You'd better make your point," he said to Hiss.

Hiss obliged. "What about Mao?"

There had been conflict within the Department concerning support for the Chinese. As Chief of the Far Eastern Division, Hamilton was the man responsible. He was in fact a Chinese language expert, but he was always "on the one hand and on the other." "Do we really know enough about Mao?" Hamilton replied.

"To hell with Mao," said Hornbeck. "What about Grew?"

Hope of a response from anyone was delayed while Joseph Ballantine noisily hammered used tobacco out of his pipe into the delicate Spode saucer of his coffee cup. The performance was in keeping with Bally's general demeanor; he was slovenly and ill-mannered. Additional evidence was the series of stains on his shirt from the earlier bowl of gazpacho.

"Max," Bally slurred out, "you just got to get your head out of China. There's no way we're gonna have much to do there. Old Vinegar Joe Stilwell is the man there now. We've got to look at the future."

Hiss gently demurred. "There must be something that can be done."

Hornbeck made up his mind to get the conversation back on the rails. As Hiss' superior he was able to cut off that source of interruption with the subtle lift of an eyebrow. A lifted hand silenced Hamilton. To Ballantine he said, "I think we have more important matters that shall be handled at my discretion." Looking across at Hamilton, he said, "Look, Max, you have your work ahead of you, you know what I mean. So why not just think about that? I will see to this matter and then you don't have to worry about it."

Hamilton did not mind at all. He was grateful to eliminate any sort of aggravation from his life; the mental demands of the past six or eight months had been quite enough.

"Why don't you run back to the Department?" Hornbeck suggested. "Alger will go along with you."

The suggestion was clearly an order. Hiss was rising before the sentence was finished.

With Hamilton and Hiss gone, Hornbeck motioned Ballantine and Priest into a huddle.

In his mellow voice, Hornbeck began, "I want to keep Hamilton out of this. He is beginning to crack under pressure. Maybe, if he stabilizes, we can bring him in, but there is no way we can depend on him right now."

Ballantine nodded assent. "I don't trust Hiss, either."

"Don't you worry about my assistant," Hornbeck came back sternly. "He is not your concern. What have you done about the August despatches?"

The question was urgent. Ballantine was at the center of the laundering operation designed to clean up and wipe out all incriminating traces of the Pearl Harbor warning-that-wasn't. Dr. Stanley Hornbeck had been long enough in the State Department to know the necessity of occasionally protecting others in order to protect oneself. Often it made the difference between survival and disgrace.

December 7, 1941 had not run its course before he knew he was likely to wind up carrying the can. More than anyone else he would bear responsibility for the long-held belief that peace with Japan was obtainable. It was true enough that much of the blame attached to those who had advised *him*, like Grew, Hamilton, Ballantine, and the rest of the motley crew. But who, in turn had passed that lunatic optimism on to Cordell Hull and, ultimately, to the President of the United States? He had.

More than 2,300 American servicemen were dead because of that, because Cordell Hull and Franklin Roosevelt thought the Japanese genuinely contemplated peace, because Yamamoto's planes had been able to come out of the sky at a slumbering, unexpecting Pearl Harbor. A substantial part of the U.S. Pacific Fleet was resting on the ocean floor.

Trouble was, there was no way he could blame it on Grew, and Grew alone. That meant Grew had to be made to look good, and *that* meant a laundering operation of heroic proportions.

He enlisted Ballantine and Priest. Ballantine was easy. He'd known Grew since Tokyo in 1936 and had been on service in the Far Eastern Division of the Department in Washington ever since. He was by inclination a bootlicker. Hornbeck set him to cleaning up the Department files, weeding out evidence of Grew's incompetence from all telegrams, letters, and despatches from Tokyo.

Mack Priest's Tokyo experience was equally invaluable: His job was applying cosmetic surgery to Grew's diaries. Grew's habit had been to peck

147

out the entries on a portable typewriter that followed him wherever he went. Grew was acutely conscious of his role in history and took care to send carbons via the diplomatic pouch to Hornbeck in Washington. It would be relatively easy to clean them up.

Grew, Hornbeck hoped, had got the message back in Tokyo and would be busy performing the same cleansing operation. If he hadn't, they were all in trouble.

Doctoring the files was a more complex business than rewriting Grew's diaries.

"The August files," Ballantine confided, leaning closer still, "are a disaster. I swear it looks as if Grew were a relative-in-law of Konoye."

"I know it does," said Hornbeck. "The Japanese Prime Minister gives that idiot dinner once a week and that's all he has to do to convince the guy peace is around the corner. I'll give him credit for it. Konoye certainly sold us a pup. And I know it looks like it from the files. Question is: Is it salvageable? Can we wipe it out, but good?"

Ballantine leaned back, looking smug. As he moved, Hornbeck and Priest noticed that Bally's tie had slipped into the coffee cup and dragged a brown stain across the white tablecloth. Bally did not notice. "I've taken care of it," he said.

His smugness angered Hornbeck; this was a serious situation that needed positive action, not complacence. "What the hell have you done?" Hornbeck shouted.

Ballantine's boldness evaporated. He hunched himself farther back. "Helen's taking care of it," he said.

Hornbeck reached across and gripped Ballantine's wrist. The hold was firm and Hornbeck

148

squeezed as he spoke. "You hear me good, Bally. No mistakes. You watch every word as if your life depended on it. You tell your friend every single word she puts down; we need that. I demand that." Helen Svoboda was one of the Department typists. It was rumored in State that Miss Svoboda was no more choosy about men than Bally was about women; their relationship was consequently on the most intimate level. Ballantine had enlisted her and three other girls to perform the mechanics of retyping the hundreds of documents which would have to be changed in order to expunge the damning evidence. Mack Priest was using another typist to work on restructuring the Grew diaries. The entire effort was huge; Grew had a habit of filing extremely long reports and his diaries ran to thirteen volumes.

Priest felt he was being left out of the conference. "It's a hell of a lot of work, Doctor," he complained. "I hope we're going in the right direction. Suppose someone gets wind of it? Suppose Grew doesn't change his diary? Hell, it could be bad."

"Don't worry about Grew," Hornbeck said. "I'll get to him fast enough. It will only be a matter of correlating what we did with what he's done. It will work."

Ballantine had been mulling over Hornbeck's rebuke. Ever since they had begun the project, he had been suffering from a nagging fear of detection. "Suppose there is an investigation? he asked.

The thought had occurred to Hornbeck. There had already been one investigation, conducted on the instructions of the President by Supreme Court Justice Owen Roberts. Hornbeck had been damn lucky, so lucky that *his* opinion had been sought on the course the investigation should take. He was more than glad to give it.

The Roberts Commission saw its task in simple terms: Somewhere out there there had to be a scapegoat. Their business was to find him, or them. The American people wanted to know who was to blame for the Pearl Harbor disaster.

It would not do to blame senior military personnel; that would be bad for morale. Besides, the generals and the admirals had to fight the war.

Nor was it possible to point the finger at senior government or diplomatic officers. That, too, would be bad for morale, bad for the war effort.

So the Roberts Commission sat for thirty-six days and decided it would be most convenient to blame the whole fiasco on Admiral Husband Kimmel and General Walter Short, senior military commanders at Pearl Harbor and therefore eminently visible candidates for shafting.

Hornbeck felt in the clear, at least for the time being. If Ballantine, Priest, and Grew did their jobs properly, they could all look forward to an untroubled future. Priest might be a foulmouthed boor, Ballantine a slovenly toady, and Grew an idiot, but under his personal guidance all would be well.

"Don't worry, boys," said Hornbeck, suppressing his distaste for the two present. "Have confidence in me."

"We have every confidence in you, Doctor," smirked Ballantine. "It's just that ... well, you know ... sometimes it dawns on you just what you're doing."

"Just concentrate on the job," said Hornbeck. "What have you done about Konoye?"

"I think it looks okay now," said Ballantine,

wiping his tie on the inside of his jacket. "I changed a few words here and there, a few inflections. I made it seem like Grew was wise to him all the time, had his doubts. You know. Like Grew knew Konoye was pretty charming but he was on his guard all the time."

"Good," said Hornbeck. "What about Kurusu?"

Kurusu was the special envoy assigned by the Japanese to Washington to convince the Americans that peace negotiations were sincere. Grew had hailed his appointment as a sure sign of peaceable intentions.

"I fixed that, too," said Ballantine. "I had Grew say he had to be watched because he was a skillful international politician. I think I used those exact words."

"Good work, Bally," said Hornbeck, rising to leave.

"You know, one thing kinda worries me," Ballantine said.

"What's that?"

"The way we're fixing it," said Ballantine. "Secretary Hull is going to look a real stupid ass. If all of this information really had been at his fingertips, then, I mean, my God, you couldn't trust the guy to cross the road without a chaperone."

Hornbeck snuffed out his cigarette and meticulously replaced his linen napkin. "Hull," he said, "is an old man."

"To hell with him," said Priest.

CHAPTER 14

NEW YORK, N.Y.

AUGUST 25, 1942

Ben Stockton had trouble believing his ears. Up on the borrowed 19th floor office over Grand Central Station, he was listening to a group of learned anthropologists lecturing to him and other members of the Office of War Information on the niceties of psychological warfare against the Japanese.

He felt lucky to have the job, even with the drawbacks. Frank Schuler had been bounced to the insignificant outpost of Antigua and Cabot Coville exiled to the Philippines. Life was otherwise somewhere near normal at State. Those who had kow-towed were safe in their jobs. Some had even managed promotion. Those with no stomach for hypocrisy—like Schuler and Coville—got busted. Or got out.

Stockton got out. His formerly excellent working relationship with Undersecretary Welles was hampered by Hamilton, obstructed by Ballantine, and eventually destroyed by Hornbeck. His personal record was strewn with damning comments like "meddlesome," "uncooperative," "insubordinate," "insolent," and "unstable." None of that seemed to bother Elmer Davis, director of OWI. His office, he told Stockton, was looking for talent, not subservience. President Roosevelt had ordered it into being within forty-eight hours of the attack on Pearl Harbor. Its object: to mount the most impressive propaganda campaign in the history of communications. That needed talent. It did not need servility.

"The Emperor of Japan," one of the anthropologists, or psychologists—Stockton had forgotten which—was intoning, "is a sacred symbol to his people. He is inviolate and omnipotent. He is God. He is, I must emphasize, an essential constituent of the psyche of his people. It is for that reason that we must refrain from direct propaganda attacks on his person."

Unable to hold it back, Stockton blurted out, "That son-of-a-bitch was in this up to his ass."

While "ass" might be an anatomical term, son-of-a-bitch is not normally part of the jargon of anthropology. The experts all turned to Stockton, glaring contempt in their eyes.

"I mean," he said, "the Emperor is a fine target for propaganda. He is a twerp, he is funny looking, and he is a goddamned enemy. I was there just about a year ago and I saw the power that guy has. I also know quite a bit about the situation in Japan and I know that he was directly involved in the formulation and execution of their war policy. He's perfect for us to go after."

One of the two female anthropologists in the room, a mannish-looking woman in her mid-thirties, said condescendingly, "We *know* his physical attributes, young man. We are considering what will happen *after* this conflict. If we are to control Japan in *any* way, then we must have the office and presence of the Emperor intact. *That* is our opinion."

153

It was the first time that Ben had ever heard anyone use a royal "our," but that was how it came out. She seemed entitled to use it; her fellow experts solemnly nodded their agreement.

At the head of the conference table, Jarvis, the OWI man who was sitting in for Director Davis asked Ben, "Do you have something to contribute other than obstreperous remarks?"

"Sorry," said Stockton, and held his peace.

The meeting droned on. Victory was inevitable; the U.S. would occupy Japan; the Emperor would be needed; no propaganda pot shots at Hirohito. It would be permissible to cast barbs at Hitler (with Spike Jones' *Right in the Fuhrer's Face*) and to ridicule Mussolini (the most massive lower jaw in human history), but the Emperor of Japan, the ruler who had named his era *"Showa"* for "enlightenment and peace" was to remain inviolate. He would serve the needs of our nation better in the future if he were not made a fool in the eyes of the American people.

And so Ben Stockton was to assume a new role in the war. He was to help insure that the leader of the country's mortal enemy was not to be abused in propaganda.

After the meeting, Stockton went to see Jarvis. "Can I have some help on this?" he asked.

"What kind?" asked Jarvis.

"Look," Ben explained, "I know Japan pretty well. But I sure could use one of the old Japan hands from State. Those guys spent years over there. They really know the Japs and they could give me a hell of a lot of good advice. What do you say?"

Jarvis considered the request for a moment. "Who?" he asked.

Ben had already given that a lot of thought. "Frank Schuler."

"Try another name."

"Hey, come on," Stockton urged. "Frank would be great." He had tried unsuccessfully on two previous occasions to get Schuler into the OWI, but each time the idea had been vetoed. "Look. The poor bastard is pigeonholed down on some island in the Caribbean just wasting away. Let me have him for this job."

Jarvis knew about Frank Schuler. When he had originally tried to get him, there had been such an explosion of anti-Schuler rockets coming out of the Department of State that there was no way he would get into that mess.

Jarvis repeated, "Try another name."

"I want Schuler," Stockton insisted. "He is talented and he can help. Now that's all I know."

"Look, Ben," Jarvis said. "Face it. This Schuler is trouble. He got himself into some kind of bad grace in State and I don't want to get into it. We've got a war to run here and I don't want it all muddied up with some inter-State Department bullshit." Stockton opened his mouth to argue further, but his boss raised his hand to cut him off. "I know you think the guy got the shaft. That's not my problem. All I know is that some pretty top-level brass in State want to keep your friend on ice and they will not turn him loose. Now don't go making more problems for us."

"He's not a friend. It's just. . . ." Stockton did not bother to finish.

"Look," said Jarvis. "I agree that it'd be good for you to have some help. What about this?" He slid a copy of the morning's *New York Times* across the desk. Ben picked it up and looked at the front page article circled near the bottom:

155

GRIPSHOLM ARRIVES TODAY
BRINGING 1,500 FROM ORIENT.

"How about that?" Jarvis asked. "The whole damned Tokyo Embassy is on that ship. You ought to find one guy you could trust to help you. Why don't you go down there and look around? I'd bet you one of them would like to go back to work on your project."

Stockton forgot Schuler for the moment. His memory was racing through the list of people he might know on the ship. Chip Bohlen, Ned Crocker, a half-dozen others might be available to work on the project. It was a great idea.

In five minutes he was down on the Lexington Avenue side of Grand Central, directing all of his energies toward finding a taxi cab to take him to the ship arrival terminal in Jersey City.

The Swedish ocean liner *Gripsholm* was moored to Pier F at the Jersey City docks and security was tight. Federal Marshals, FBI Agents, Immigration and Naturalization inspectors supported Port Authority police in keeping back both journalists and visitors. No exuberant fanfare greeted the 1,451 passengers who were being returned to the United States after internment by the Japanese in Tokyo and the Far East. Months of diplomatic negotiations had finally resulted in an exchange of nationals and the Americans had made the 18,000-mile sea voyage home.

There was no noisy welcome. Word had been circulated for public consumption that the various law agencies involved were conducting a careful screening to detect any illegal entrants among the passengers. In fact this was part, but only part, of the explanation for the quiet, almost clandestine arrival. A month before, onboard the *Drottningsholm*, arriving on a similar mission from Europe, the FBI had discovered a Nazi spy who had since been convicted of espionage and sentenced to death.

The real reason for the tight security and lack of celebration was being explained in a spacious stateroom up on the promenade deck of the *Gripsholm*.

"What do you mean he won't see me. That is patently ridiculous!" Joseph Grew's voice was cracking with anger and tension.

Dr. Stanley Hornbeck displaced a lot of air with his delicate hands, signaling to the recent Ambassador to Japan to lower his voice.

"Don't try to hush me, Stanley." Grew shouted. "What do you mean?"

They were standing in the middle of the suite's parlor. Grew's wife, Alice, heard him shouting. "What's wrong, Joe?" she asked, appearing at the door.

Grew took control of himself, went to her, and said, "Nothing, my dear. Just finish getting our things ready. We should be going down in a few minutes." She smiled over Grew's shoulder at Hornbeck and Hamilton. "Now we have been through a lot, Stanley and Max," she pleaded. "Don't get the Ambassador overwrought."

The two men forced grins as Hornbeck answered for both of them. "Not at all, Alice. Just business as usual. Your husband is so important."

Placated, Alice allowed herself to be bustled out.

Thrusting his lanky frame back to the middle of the parlor, Grew repeated his demand: "What do you mean?"

Hornbeck rubbed his cheek and felt the rare

presence of a beard stubble; he had rushed from Washington by train to New York on orders from the Secretary of State. Grew was to be advised that President Roosevelt "did not wish to see him at present." The rush had been in order to get that word to Grew before he met the press and made some grand statement about being anxious to meet with the President.

"For the time being," said Hornbeck, "the President does not plan to see you."

Anger flared again in Grew's eyes and Hornbeck decided that he might as well get all of the bad news out. "And the Secretary has been advised to tell you that he would be busy for 'several weeks.'"

Grew's eyes went wide. He brought his hands up to his temples. He staggered across the cabin and sat clumsily in an armchair. Hornbeck and Hamilton walked around the coffee table and sat on the sofa.

Weakly, Grew said, "My God, what is going on?"

Hornbeck allowed Grew a while to get himself together. "Things have been rather difficult in the Department, Joe," he said as calmly as he could. "The President is angry with our performance as far as the Far East was concerned. He feels he has been betrayed."

"Come now, Stanley," Grew said in a steady voice. "He has to know that we worked under impossible conditions."

"Joe," Hornbeck said, "the Secretary is getting on in years. The failure of our efforts with the Japanese has taken a lot out of him. At first, right after the attack, he was able to vent his anger on Nomura and Kurusu. Later he began to wonder where he had ever got the idea we would be able to prevent war. Then the Roberts Commission held their hearings and there was such a gap in the case against Kimmel and Short that he began looking inside."

"Inside?"

Hornbeck nodded. "Within the Department. He was too exhausted to do much digging, but he did get the feeling he had been given faulty information."

Grew protested. "What faulty information? How was I to know? How was anyone to know? I really felt we could outsmart their militarists. Even after Tojo came in, I met with him; I felt he would be able to control the military."

Hornbeck nodded impatiently. "I know you did and you said so in one of your despatches."

Grew's eyes snapped at Hornbeck and the famous tic showed as he jerked his neck. He looked first at Hamilton and then back at Hornbeck. "Can we talk alone?"

Hornbeck looked confused. "You mean without Max?"

Grew nodded.

Hornbeck said, "It's all right. Max knows."

Grew's tic jumped violently. "You mean about the note you sent. About being 'prepared'?"

Hornbeck nodded. "He knows."

Grew breathed a sigh. "Max," he said, "I am so glad you are with us. I don't know what I would do without your help."

"Thank you, Mr. Ambassador," Hamilton said listlessly. He had little taste for intrigue, particularly intrigue which could get him into trouble. But once drawn into a mess like that, it was difficult to wriggle out again gracefully.

A happy thought occurred to Grew. He jumped

159

with excitement. "The car!" he said. "Did you get the car?"

"We got it," said Hamilton.

"Is it here?" Grew pleaded. "Here at the dock?"

"No, Mr. Ambassador," said Hamilton, disgruntled.

Grew had spent his last several weeks in captivity pestering Washington to buy him a new Lincoln Zephyr. The Far Eastern Division had more pressing matters to attend to, but at the expense of a great deal of trouble and energy, the Ambassador's Zephyr had been rounded up.

"Why not?" complained Grew. "I was really looking forward to seeing it. A simple thing like that. I am an Ambassador, you know."

"We know," said Hamilton.

"Oh well," said Grew. "As long as it has the right upholstery and the right shade of . . . "

"Screw the auto, Joe," said Hornbeck. "You've got more important things to worry about. What did you do about the documents in Tokyo?"

Grew came back to reality.

"Gene Dooman and I worked on them."

Hornbeck asked, "Anyone else?"

Grew nodded. "Penny Morton."

Hornbeck looked to Hamilton. "She's fine," he said. "Very trustworthy. We can have her work with Jane Barton and they should tidy things up quickly."

Grew cocked his head. "Jane Barton?"

"She's with us," said Hornbeck. "This whole thing has not been easy, Joe. We're a long way from being through, but we do have a really tight control. You can't imagine what is involved in—how should I say this—'studying,' that's it, studying several years of correspondence."

Grew plopped back in his chair. To no one in particular he said, "What are we involved in?"

In a way, Hornbeck could understand Grew's attitude; the man had just arrived home after an internment that could not have been especially nice, and he was deeply involved in a project that could not really be considered admirable by a man immersed in tradition and protocol. In addition, Grew had just been slapped down by the President.

But Hornbeck's sympathy was tempered by a lively awareness of his own position, and the position of a dozen or so others, all to some degree implicated in the cover-up operation that Grew's idiocy had made necessary. If this one blew up, it could take the best part of the Foreign Service with it. The Great Unwashed would flood down the corridors of State. All those delicate immunities—from the press, from the military, from the ignorant bastards in Congress who thought a seat on Capitol Hill gave them carte blanche to meddle in foreign affairs—all those immunities, painstakingly built up over decades, would be destroyed. It was bad enough that Roosevelt felt free to interfere with State, and free to appoint a Tennessee deadhead like Hull to run the Department for him. Undersecretary Welles was no gift to diplomacy either. And lately, Hornbeck had been detecting, to his horror, distinct signs of insubordination in the middle ranks. Schuler and Coville were prime examples. But that sort of rabble he could deal with. *If* Grew didn't blow it.

Hornbeck assumed his best and smoothest schoolmaster's tone. "We are protecting everything we believe in, Joe. We are not engaged in anything immoral. We are ensuring that our

161

country has at least some future on the international stage. Can you imagine what the military establishment would do if they were able to grab hold of this matter? They would crush us, and diplomacy for decades to come would be in the hands of the Admirals and Generals. Foreign policy would be planned in war rooms and would be carried out on the battlefields. We must fight to protect the future."

Grew digested Hornbeck's lecture as it was delivered. "You are so right," he said enthusiastically. "That's why it's so important for me to see the President!"

"God-dammit," Hornbeck exploded. "You can't see the President and that's that."

"Oh, all right, Stanley. If you say so." Grew slumped back, deflated.

Hornbeck relaxed. He had won. "Of course not, Joe. That old cripple has come and he will go, but the Department will have to continue. It is our job to ensure that we remain unblemished." He threw Grew some flattery to make him feel better. "Your place in history is assured," he said. "You will be known as the man who warned them. The politicians will have to take blame for their lack of insight. The military has already taken its thrashing for its own failure. It was not your fault that the military failed to defend against attack. Think of it, man, who was really at fault?"

Grew thought for a moment. He had little doubt. "We cannot attack them too strongly. We could have been a little more emphatic, though."

"Forget that," said Hornbeck. "We did our best. Just remember that. The politicians and the military screwed it up. Let them commit group suicide if that's their pleasure. We did all that

162

was humanly possible, and that's what the record shows."

"Are you quite sure about that? About the record, I mean?" Grew asked hesitantly.

"Joe, you know as much about that as I do," said Hornbeck. "You know how easy it is for the written word to lie. But errors can be corrected, you know that, too. We've been correcting the records to protect the Department, and we've done a damn good job. You'll have nothing to worry about if you've executed your part of it."

Groping, Grew asked, "Is it possible? Dooman and I did all we could before we left Japan. We even changed several of my diary entries. But not too much."

Hornbeck smiled and said, "Joe, we've had Mack Priest going through the copy you sent me of your diary. There is more than 'not too much' to be changed."

Grew winced. "Priest? What does he know? How could he tamper with my thoughts?"

Hornbeck stiffened. "You must trust me, Joe. Priest was the best man I had. He was the man most recently in your Embassy; he knew the problem. Don't worry, I kept a tight check on him."

Abstractedly, as if he was pulling up a distasteful memory, Grew said, "Dooman wanted to change more, too, but I wouldn't let him. There are some things that simply cannot be changed; they are too important."

"The only important thing is our mutual futures, Joe," Hornbeck reminded him. "Face that. We will do what we must. If your diaries have to be changed, then they will be."

Grew sat there for a moment, his head moving back and forth.

Hornbeck was impatient. The time for Grew to

leave the boat was close. Angrily he said, "What the hell does that mean?"

Grew said, "We won't be able to change much."

"Why?"

"*Collier's* Magazine," said Grew proudly, "has asked to print some of my diary."

"What?"

"They cabled me when we stopped in Rio. I've promised to let them print a series of excerpts."

Another "What?" from Hornbeck.

"They are meeting me this morning when I disembark. I've had Dooman getting the diaries together so I could show their editor what is involved."

"Oh, my God!" said Hamilton.

Grew shifted uneasily in his chair. "Gentlemen," he said, "there are some things that must be said to the people of our country. I have a duty to our nation, an obligation to history. Surely you can see where it is vital for such a message to get the best exposure possible? *Collier's* Magazine will be a perfect forum for my words."

Hamilton had trouble getting the words out. "Surely, Mr. Ambassador," he muttered, "you are not serious."

"I don't know what you mean, Max," Grew snapped. "Gene Dooman and I worked very hard. We changed the piece about the Peruvian Ambassador's Pearl Harbor warning and we modified more than a dozen other items. I don't think I could be asked to do much more. Remember that those words of mine are the things of which history is made."

Hornbeck sprang out of his seat and paced across the parlor. Ignoring Grew's last words, he asked, "What arrangements have you made?"

"I am to meet their editor on the dock," Grew

164

boasted, "and give him the important diaries. Then we are to have dinner tonight. I think that is satisfactory."

Hornbeck spun around, shouting, "Joe, you must be unbalanced! There will be *no* meeting. You will give them *nothing*!"

"But I gave them my word."

"Then you damn well have to break it. Make some excuse. We must have time to check what you are going to give them."

"But," Grew pleaded, "they will be in a hurry. They said as much to me in their correspondence."

"They will have to wait," said Hornbeck.

Grew's shoulders sagged. "If you insist."

On the way down to the gangway, Hornbeck managed to get Grew's attention out of earshot of the entourage. "Listen, Joe. Tell the *Collier's* people that you will have to see them in a few days. We can get the bulk of the work done by then. Okay?"

Grew nodded his understanding.

As they reached the bottom of the gangplank, Hamilton caught up to Grew and handed him a typewritten paper.

"What's this?" Grew asked impatiently.

Hamilton replied, "I didn't have time to give it to you in the cabin, Mr. Ambassador. It is the guidelines for what you are to say to the press."

Grew snapped the paper from Hamilton and gave it a quick glance. "How dare you suggest something like this?" he growled.

"It's not me, Mr. Ambassador. It is on direction of the White House. They want you to keep your remarks within those guidelines."

Grew huffed. "The insolent brass of it all."

"Those are orders, sir."

Grew reread the message. "He really hates me, doesn't he, Max?"

Maxwell Hamilton looked down at the dirty concrete of the dock and tried to distract himself by studying nothing.

"Max?"

Hamilton looked up and stared at Grew. He could not bring himself to speak what he knew; he merely nodded his head.

Grew stiffened and walked away. He climbed into the limousine and was driven toward the end of the dock where the press was waiting behind a fence.

Alone, Hornbeck and Hamilton watched Grew pull away.

"It is going to be rough on him," said Hamilton.

Hornbeck grimaced. "It's going to be rough on all of us, Max. I just hope he's smart enough to stay clear of the President. It could end up being a historic first: a murder by a President."

CHAPTER 15

MIAMI, FLORIDA

JANUARY 11, 1943

The Florida East Coast Railway locomotive 714 pulled easily through the night. The headlight stabbed ahead through the raindrops. In the cab the engineer signaled to his fireman. The fireman adjusted a valve, backing off the steam pressure, and the train began easing down from its modest 35 miles an hour. They were coming to the end of their journey.

"Everything okay?" came a voice from the jumpseat at the rear of the cab.

Only the fireman turned around to look back as he said, "Sure. Great." That was for the benefit of the Secret Service man who otherwise might feel a bit left out of the picture.

On the two-day trip from Washington to Miami, the train, code-named POTUS, had telegraphed ahead for the clear track which was due the President of the United States.

There were only five cars on the train. Franklin Roosevelt was on the first leg of the historic journey that would take him to the Casablanca Conference. The first two cars carried White House staff personnel who would not be making the Atlantic crossing, but who had been needed for the working trip to Florida. Then came a regular Pullman dining car. That was followed by the executive car, *Conneaut*, occupied by the aides and officials who would be boarding seaplanes for the flight to North Africa from the Naval base at Miami's Dinner Key.

The final car in the train was the *Ferdinand Magellan*, U.S. Car No. One, a luxurious, custom-built private railway car made exclusively for the use of the President. The American Railway Association had seen to the manufacture of the car which, for security reasons, was painted in the usual Pullman green. It had a large storage area at the front end. Then came the galley, pantry, and servants' quarters, then the four bedrooms specially designed for the President. At the end of the car was an elegant conference room furnished with modest but excellent pieces of mahogany.

At the six-foot, highly polished dining table, Senator Alben Barkley moved slightly against the striped satin-damask upholstery and waited for Franklin Roosevelt to resume speaking.

Senator Barkley had boarded POTUS a couple of hours earlier at West Palm Beach during a stop that had been made especially to pick him up. Barkley had been flown from Louisville, Kentucky, to Palm Beach on orders from President Roosevelt.

Roosevelt was up and dressed when Barkley was escorted into the conference room. The President had aged over the past few years, but he looked bright, happy, and anxious to be about the business of his office.

After the customary pleasantries, Roosevelt came quickly to the point. "Alben, I've got a big job for you. Do you want it?"

People high within the Democratic Party, especially those who had any hope of furthering their careers, knew that they could not hedge with FDR. When he offered a job, you did not ask for details. You said yes.

Barkley said, "Yes, sir."

"Good." FDR smiled and lit his cigarette.

Roosevelt, without preamble, gave him the essence of it: "I want a full-scale Congressional investigation into the Pearl Harbor mess."

The Senator's portly frame registered surprise. "I thought there had already been an investigation, Mr. President."

"Of course there was a damn investigation," said Roosevelt. "There had to be an investigation, and quick. We had to demonstrate to the people

168

of this country that we were as anxious as they were to find out the cause of Pearl Harbor."

"Well," said Barkley, "didn't we?"

"Come on, Alben," said the President. "You've been a pro long enough to smell a rat when it's good and dead and stinking to heaven. They tied the can to the Army and Navy at Pearl. That was, to understate the facts, a superficial judgment. Army and Navy will be holding their own boards of inquiry. Can't say I blame them. Those poor chaps took a pretty good lacing here at home about that. They want their day and, by God, I think they deserve it."

"Won't that clear it up, Mr. President?"

"I am afraid not, Alben. They'll give it a pretty good shot, but I think there will be too much in their way."

"I don't understand, sir."

Roosevelt jammed his cigarette down into the ashtray on the table. "Damn it, Barkley, I'm not going to do your job. I am merely trying to prod you in the right direction. The military boys won't get a fair shake because they don't have the authority to pry open some of the doors that will be locked against them. The Congress can do it; you have the strength. I will back you with an Executive Order; with your own strength and my backing, you'll be able to get to the bottom of it."

"But what is there to know? That's what I don't understand, Mr. President. Is there something that you are privy to?"

"You are aware, Alben," the President said, "that I have one or two political opponents in this country? Enemies, you might even call them?"

"I had heard there were one or two of those misguided fellas around, sir," said Barkley. "I think they call them Republicans."

"Oh, there're good Republicans, Alben. You know that. Well, there's one or two. It's those isolationist sons-of-bitches I'm talking about. Roosevelt's war, they're calling it. *My* war. Now they're putting the word around that Japan was a poor little picked-on country that never would have dreamed of an episode like Pearl Harbor if it hadn't been for Franklin Roosevelt making pacts with Winston Churchill, doing all he damnwell could to ensure this country went to war."

"I know that's bullshit, Mr. President."

"Malicious bullshit, Senator. But sometimes that substance sticks. If this country's got to be at war, then I want all the people to know *why* we're at war."

"I agree, sir."

Roosevelt pointed to a wall photograph of himself in yachting gear. "You know how I love the Navy," he said, "and you can imagine how much it pains me to see anything happen to the Navy. Yet these people suggest that I *allowed* Pearl Harbor to happen. My God, it would have been so simple to have had the fleet out at sea on December 7, if there *had* been any warning. We could have let the attack take place and not suffered those fantastic losses. Those bastards know that, but they're determined to fix the blame right on my shoulders.

"Mind you," the President continued, "I'd take the weight if I had to. I'd be happy to if it were true or would do any good. But it isn't and it won't."

"Do you have any ideas?" Barkley asked.

Roosevelt lit another cigarette. "I have knowledge, Alben. Not ideas, but knowledge. Hull and I were fed such a line of crap by the Department of State that we were lulled into thinking that we might be able to delay a war. But those bastards who were charged with the responsibility of informing us gave us a bag of garbage. Do you know that I sent a message to the Japs offering to meet with them personally? God, I would have gone any place, any time, to head off this war. Yet, silly as it might seem, there were people who knew the dangers. Did you ever read that Drew Pearson article right after the attack?"

"I missed it," Barkley admitted.

"In the summer of 1941, a group of experts in State wrote a memo saying that war was coming. Do you realize the import of that? I never heard of that memo; Hull never heard of that memo; yet, the truth was right under our noses, carefully and conscientiously put down. It was like a red flag waving and we didn't see it. And all I was getting was just damn drivel from Grew in Tokyo, and Hornbeck feeding me crap. No wonder the Navy and Army were caught with their pants down at Pearl, no wonder I was lulled. We were relying on the Department of State and those morons were busy peering up their own asses."

"I scarcely know those names you mentioned, Mr. President," Barkley said.

"You will," said the President.

The train was moving through Hollywood, Florida. FDR pointed to the view. "Lovely town," he said. "Tom Dewey always comes here."

Barkley smiled. "That name I know, Mr. President."

FDR bellowed at that reaction. The laughter was loud enough to prompt FDR's steward to pop his head out of the pantry. The President took advantage of his sudden appearance.

171

"I'll have some tea, Clinton," he said.

"Yes, sir. We should be in Miami in about 45 minutes."

"Good, good. What about you, Alben?"

Barkley hesitated. "No . . . no thanks."

FDR cajoled him. "Come on. What about a drink?"

Barkley was tired but he could use a drink. He turned to the steward. "Bourbon and branch," he ordered.

The servant smiled broadly and ducked back into the pantry. In a couple of minutes both men were enjoying their refreshments. But Barkley had used the time to collect his thoughts. As he sipped his drink, he asked, "When do you want the hearings, Mr. President?"

Roosevelt had thought that through. "Not for a while. We have a war to win first. It will take time, but we're rolling. I'm not going to guess how long this war will run. The Japanese won't give up easily. It could be two, three, four years."

"That seems a long time to wait," said Barkley.

"True enough," the President said. "A lot will happen in that time. But any earlier and it might hurt the war effort. We must keep that in mind, Alben. We cannot hinder our goal. But there is a lot you can be doing. You will need to get a good committee. I don't want a bunch of political hacks on this; we need probing minds. And you will need time to line up a good counsel. Do you have any ideas?"

"You've caught me offguard, sir. I would have to think."

"You have time; that's what I mean. But you must have some bright man you could entrust to do a considerable job, don't you?"

Barkley was not a man who gave the appearance of moving swiftly, but his mind worked rapidly. "There is Gesell," he said. "I like him."

"Gerhard Gesell?"

"Yes."

"He would be good. I like him, too." A toothy grin erupted as FDR said, "There, you see why I asked for you to handle this. Gesell would be simply grand for that job. He'd dig in and not let loose. Good man, Barkley, good man."

For the remainder of the journey President and Senator discussed avenues that the investigation should explore. Roosevelt emphasized that he wanted every aspect of the State Department's involvement dug up and examined. He mentioned Hornbeck and Grew specifically.

"The Grew you mention," Barkley asked, "is he the guy you sent out making those 'Our Enemy Japan' speeches?"

"Exactly."

Barkley nodded. "But, Mr. President, I thought you were rather fond of him. I heard someplace that he had helped you with your stamp collection."

FDR clenched his teeth. "If he was as good a statesman as he was a stamp dealer, we might not be fighting the Japs today. Sure he got me stamps. I was rather fond of him. He had a good presence and he was so damned lengthy in his communications I felt he was competent. I should have known better. Fact is, he hadn't the first idea about what was going on right around him in Tokyo. You'll see it all when you begin to investigate. It will all be there in his telegrams and despatches. Wait until you read some of those damned documents. When they weren't knee-deep in double-talk, they were virtually Japanese Government handouts. Wait until you read them."

173

"I'm looking forward to it, sir."

The train was coming to an expertly paced stop at the Florida East Coast terminal in Miami, and FDR's staff began to appear down at the front end of the car. "Well, Alben," said FDR in parting, "you begin digging in. I'll be back in a couple of weeks and we can talk again. But you start getting your ideas together. As soon as the end of the war is in sight, we'll go to work on getting those bastards. I want the blame laid where it is due, Alben. You'll see to that for me, won't you?"

"I will, Mr. President," the Senator promised. "I surely will."

"Damned good," said FDR. "Now I've got to be off on our country's business." He glanced in amusement at Barkley's quizzical expression. "You'd like to know where I'm going, wouldn't you, Alben?"

"Only at your pleasure, sir."

"Casablanca, Barkley, Casablanca. By God we're going to win this war even with the handicap those people in State gave to our enemies."

Senator Barkley was lost in the swirl of presidential aides and assistants. It would be nearly eighteen months before he could pound down the gavel to open the Hearings Before the Joint Committee on the Investigation of the Pearl Harbor Attack.

Many battles would be fought before then and many lives lost, but Japan would still be fighting.

CHAPTER 16

WASHINGTON, D.C.

JULY 6, 1946

Ben Stockton hesitated before pressing the buzzer outside Frank Schuler's apartment in the Broadmoor.

The war years had been rough on him. Many had lived through the hostilities buoyed up by a patriotism which made nearly any hardship acceptable. Only when the war was over did the balloon burst. Most people expected that and were ready for it. But Stockton's had burst long before.

He felt he had done a commendable job in the Office of War Information. No one told him otherwise. He had always worked hard and sometimes accomplished more than was asked of him. But he was dropped. "Cutting back on personnel," they told him. He knew it was a lie: The OWI was busier than ever when he was let go.

There were other incidents. He had heard through a close friend in the Navy Department of an opening for a Japanese expert with the War Plans Division. He applied for it. The Division was enthusiastic—until they ran a routine check with his previous employers, the State Department. Suddenly, mysteriously, "the post has been filled."

He had tried for a job with the U.S. forces in Europe. Same result. In despair he applied for an assignment to the most insignificant Consulate in Central America. His expertise was not required.

He spent the rest of the war in a middle-level job in the Office of Price Administration, whose contribution to the war effort was to try to see to it that the domestic economy remained reasonably stable and that consumer goods were, within reason, available. His intimate knowledge of Japanese affairs was of little use in the Gasoline Rationing Department.

Now the war was over and the Office of Price Administration was going out of business.

Schuler had called him out of the blue: How would he like to go to Japan for the State Department?

It took Schuler ten minutes to convince Stockton he wasn't kidding, and it took Stockton half an hour to get his formal application filed with the Department. It cleared in two days. He still could not believe the turnaround in his fortunes. He knew there had been some upheaval at State. President Truman had brought in Edward Stettinius from the private business sector to shake some of the dust from the Department. Some heads had rolled. Grew and Hornbeck were being eased out as quickly as possible, but they had done their work well and efficiently. The State Department was riddled with their protégés and would remain so for years.

Still, there seemed to be some latitude for innovation. Schuler had been appointed Associate Chief of Division, Japanese-Korean Branch, Area Division V—Occupied Areas (ADO), Department of State, and wanted Stockton working with him.

Stockton accepted even before looking in the new Department Register to see what it meant.

"Area Division V," said the register, "is responsible for the initiation, within the Department, of policies and programs in the fields of information and cultural affairs for the reorientation of the peoples of the occupied areas: Germany, Austria, Trieste, Japan, and Korea." It sounded like a good job to Stockton.

He had tried to see Schuler at the Department building, but Schuler had insisted on the telephone that the first meeting should be at his apartment. "It would be better, you know what I mean," he had said.

Stockton answered half-jokingly, "Have you gone paranoid on me, Frank?"

"You'd have to be crazy not to be a little paranoid, Ben," Schuler answered. "I'll see you at my apartment. About one o'clock tomorrow."

Now one o'clock had come and Stockton still hesitated about pushing the door buzzer. Suppose some of the old guard had gotten to Frank? Suppose this was to be another one of those crashing disappointments he had experienced before? Suppose Grew and his cronies had thrust their evil hands into the pot again? There was only one way to find out. He pressed the buzzer.

The door opened quickly and Schuler greeted him with a broad grin. Stockton thought he had aged noticeably in three years. His hair was snow-white and there were creases around his mouth and the corners of his eyes.

The living room of the apartment was, as Stockton expected, well furnished. He noted the baby-grand piano that he knew was Mrs. Schuler's prize possession.

"How is Olive?" Stockton asked.

Schuler laughed at the immediate connection between his wife and the highly polished piano. "Just fine, Ben," he said. "Take a seat. You'll see her in a while. She's gone out shopping so we can have a couple of hours alone."

Schuler accepted a cigarette and asked, "Are you ready to go back to Japan?"

Stockton nodded. "I hope you don't mind my asking," he said, "but how did this all happen? You and I have been on the local shit-list for quite a while."

"I can't give you a solid answer," Schuler said. "Really, I simply can't. I've spent most of the war trying to get some reasonable assignment, but I was blocked at every turn. But, with the Occupation going on under MacArthur, I guess they are desperate. I'm pleased as hell."

Ben had to slide some brown paper-covered books aside in order to reach the ashtray. He could not help but notice the title printed in black.

PEARL HARBOR ATTACK

HEARINGS

BEFORE THE

JOINT COMMITTEE ON THE

INVESTIGATION OF THE

PEARL HARBOR ATTACK

CONGRESS OF THE UNITED STATES

SEVENTY-NINTH CONGRESS

FIRST SESSION

PURSUANT TO

S. Con. Res. 27

79th Congress

A CONCURRENT RESOLUTION

AUTHORIZING AN INVESTIGATION OF

THE ATTACK ON PEARL HARBOR ON

DECEMBER 7, 1941, AND EVENTS AND

CIRCUMSTANCES RELATING THERETO

PART 1
November 15, 16, 17, 19, 20, and 21, 1945

Printed for the use of the
Joint Committee on the Investigation of the
Pearl Harbor
Attack

Vol. 61

United States
Government Printing Office
Washington: 1946

"Homework?"

Frank shook his head. "No. It's become an avocation. Some might call it an obsession, but I'll never let that happen. I'm just trying to figure out how they got away with it."

Stockton knew the "they" implied Grew, Hornbeck, and the others who had also been responsible for nearly wrecking his life, what he did not know was what Frank meant. "Got away with what?" he asked.

Schuler smiled grimly. "Hey, Ben," he said. "Come on now. You know what I'm talking about."

Stockton picked up one of the volumes and said, "I'd only have to guess, really, Frank. What do you mean?"

A change came across Schuler's normally genial countenance. He was stern as he gestured to the stacks of reports from the Joint Committee's hearings. "Look," he said with near impatience. "Look at all of this. Forty volumes of reports. Millions of words. Detailed, probing interrogation by some of the brightest men in the Congress. The perceptive and alert mind of Gerhard Gesell as Chief Assistant Counsel. All of that, and nowhere, not in one specific case, does anyone point a finger at the guilty parties! Hornbeck managed to continue his particular skill at double-talk and Grew charmed his way through several days of pontification. But does the conflict show up? They have done one hell of a job."

"The Committee?"

"Hell no," Frank snapped back. "Grew and the others. Come on, Ben. You've heard about it haven't you? The doctoring of the documents?"

Ben's lower jaw dropped. "About *what*?"

Frank stiffened. "Don't kid with me, Ben. Nearly everyone in the Department knows about it. Don't try to snow me."

"I'm not kidding you, Frank," Ben protested. "Look, you have to remember I've been out of the Department for four years. I haven't even been in the building for three years. What the hell are you talking about?"

"You haven't heard about what they are calling 'Bally's Boondoggle'?"

"You mean Ballantine?" Stockton asked.

Frank nodded. "Or 'Hamilton's Hoax'?"

"Max Hamilton? I thought he was out, or getting out."

"Right," Frank came back, "but he did his share."

"Of what, for God's sake, Frank. What?"

Schuler was plainly angry and Ben was not sure the anger wasn't directed at him. "The bastards have changed every piece of paper that shows how they fouled up on Pearl Harbor. Don't tell me you don't know, Ben. You have to."

Stockton shook his head. "I heard there was some confusion about Grew's message on the Peruvian's warning," he said, "but that was only supposed to be confusion."

"Where'd you hear it?" Schuler snapped.

Stockton forced his memory to work. "It was one of the girls in the typing pool. I took her out to dinner a couple of years back. Mabel somebody, I can't remember her name but she was cute; or Barbara Ellens, maybe not. I dated several of them. But she just mentioned there was some kind of confusion."

"Confusion!" Frank yelled, "I guess so. The bastard lied through his teeth. Grew did. They nearly got him though, they were so close, but he slipped right through it. Look at this."

Frank's hands flew in search of one of the Joint Committee Report volumes. He grabbed at one, discarded it impatiently, then grabbed at another. Finally, after several furious tries, he found what he wanted. He thrust it at Ben and ordered, "Read this."

TESTIMONY OF JOSEPH CLARK GREW, FORMER AMBASSADOR TO JAPAN

Mr. Gesell. Mr. Grew, will you state your full name for the record, please.

Mr. Grew. Joseph Grew.

Mr. Gesell. During what period of time were you our Ambassador to Japan?

Mr. Grew. I arrived in Japan on June 6, 1932; left on June 25, 1942.

Mr. Gesell. And you were there more or less continuously during that period, particularly during 1941, were you not?

Mr. Grew. Yes, sir.

Mr. Gesell. Now, if the committee please, before proceeding with Mr. Grew I want to direct specific attention to exhibit 15 in evidence, a series of three dispatches from Mr. Grew to the Department of State dated January 27, November 3. (1475) and November 17, 1941, respectively. I would like to read portions of these into the record.

The dispatch of January 27, 1941 states:

My Peruvian colleague told a member of my staff that he had heard from many sources including a Japanese source that the Japanese military forces planned, in the event of trouble with the United States, to attempt a surprise mass attack on Pearl Harbor using all of their various facilities. He added that although the project seemed fantastic, the fact that he had heard it from many sources prompted him to pass on the information.

Mr. Gesell. I notice in your book, which I am sure will be referred to from time to time here, your note of that day, for January 27, 1941, in which you say:

(1478) There is a lot of talk around town to the effect that the Japanese in case of a break with the United States are planning to go all out in a surprise mass attack on Pearl Harbor. Of course, I informed our Government.

Your reference to "a lot of talk around town" suggests that at that time you had heard the same rumor from sources other than the Peruvian Ambassador; is that correct?

Mr. Grew. Yes, sir.

Mr. Gesell. Could you indicate to what extent there was talk around town at that time?

Mr. Grew. I wouldn't say that talk was widespread, but it came from various sources. I could not now recollect from what sources, because they were not important, but this telegram which I sent on January 27 was based practically entirely on the report which had been brought to me by my Peruvian colleague.

Mr. Gesell. Did that talk persist of a general rumor category or did it prevail only at or about the time of your dispatch?

Mr. Grew. I would say only about the time of my dispatch.

Mr. Gesell. You don't remember any talk about town subsequent to that concerning a surprise attack on Pearl Harbor?

Mr. Grew. No, sir: I do not.

(1480) Mr. Gesell. I suppose you received rumors second-hand, so to speak, through your other diplomatic colleagues who themselves may have been in touch with Japanese; is that correct?

Mr. Grew. Yes, of course I received reports of what was going on from diplomatic colleagues constantly during all that year.

Mr. Gesell. Did you get from any of your diplomatic colleagues any information indicating that Japan was to attack the United States at any point subsequent to January 27, which was of a specific military nature?

Mr. Grew. I couldn't put my finger on any one conversation which would confirm that, but all the evidence which we accumulated during those years intensified as time went on, made it abundantly clear that they were likely to attack.

Mr. Gesell. I want to ask you about that in a moment, but now let me ask you this.

This report that I have been discussing indicates that on December 1 the cabinet council met and approved the commencement of hostilities against the United States.

(1482) Were you aware that there was a cabinet meeting in December, around December 1 or 2?

Mr. Grew. I recollect we were informed at that time of such a meeting.

Mr. Gesell. Was any announcement made or any information made available to you in any way indicating that one of the matters considered at the cabinet meeting was the commencement of hostilities against the United States by an attack at Pearl Harbor?

Mr. Grew. No, sir. That was all guess work.

Mr. Gesell. Did you guess that that had been considered at that time?

Mr. Grew. Yes, sir.

Mr. Gesell. Did you report that you had so guessed, to the State Department?

Mr. Grew. Well, I think that my reports were

complete in themselves. I think that the warnings that I had issued covered the field. I very likely did report that meeting but I cannot tell you without consulting our files.

Mr. Gesell. You don't recall, do you, any specific report that you made at that time to the effect that you thought the cabinet was considering an attack on Pearl Harbor?

Mr. Grew. I don't recollect any specific report to that effect. I would have to consult the records on that.

(1483) Mr. Gesell. I think we have your dispatch concerning the cabinet meeting. I will bring it forward in a moment.

Now I would like to ask you a general question.

First I have this dispatch, your dispatch of December 1 to the Department of State, and with reference to the cabinet meeting the information that you appear to have given at that time was to this effect:

Tonight's newspapers report that the Cabinet at its meeting today, while realizing the difficulty of adjusting the respective positions of the two countries, nevertheless determined to continue the Washington conversations.

(1484) Mr. Gesell. Does that refresh your recollection that you did not at that time have any information that you reported indicating that one of the matters discussed was the possibility of a Pearl Harbor attack?

Mr. Grew. I doubt if I reported that precise point at that time.

"My God," Stockton said as he pulled his eyes away from the testimony. "He lied through his teeth, just as you said."

Schuler's voice showed his anger. "Of course he

did, Ben. You know what that despatch was. All of us saw it when it came in. Even Olive saw it. He said in the original that he 'placed no credence in Schreiber's story.' Now, before the Committee he changes a few words and it makes him look like a prophet."

"But, Frank, this is easy to remedy. There's the original. It's in the files."

Frank took the volume of the report and tossed it angrily onto the floor. "It's missing. Can you believe that? It's missing!"

"I can't buy that, Frank. It's just not possible."

Frank crossed the room and went to his desk which was cluttered with stacks of documents. He pulled out the copy of a document and gave it to Ben. "See this?" he asked.

Ben took the paper and read it.

1042   CONGRESSIONAL INVESTIGATION
PEARL HARBOR ATTACK

EXHIBIT NO. 15

TELEGRAM RECEIVED

From

KD   Tokyo
This telegram must be   Dated January 27, 1941
closely paraphrased be-   Rec'd. 8:38 a.m.
fore being communicated
to anyone. (D)
Secretary of State,
   Washington
   125, January 27, 6 P.M.

My Peruvian Colleague told a member of my staff that he had heard from many sources including a Japanese source that the Japanese military forces planned, in the event of trouble with the United States, to attempt a surprise attack on Pearl Harbor using all of their military facilities. He added that although the project seemed fantastic the fact that he had heard it from many sources prompted him to pass on the information.

Ben looked confused.

"Well, what the hell is it?" Frank snapped.

Ben looked back at the paper and replied, "A telegram."

"Right," Frank said with obvious relief, then continued, "And what did Grew talk about?" Without waiting for a reply, he answered his own question, "A despatch. Remember, right when the hearing first started, Gesell asked about a 'dispatch' and Grew played his little game of semantics. Hell, the most junior man in the Department knows the difference between a despatch and a telegram. It was in the despatch that Grew had discounted the credibility of Schreiber's report; that's why none of the military were alerted, that's why the President never knew the immensity of the threat. Those bastards Grew and Hornbeck were feeding the Secretary and President rotten, biased information. So Grew played his game, stayed with the telegram concept, and never got into the contents of the despatch which he had sent in the diplomatic pouch. Hell, it wouldn't have done any good; the despatch had been destroyed."

"It's all impossible, Frank. People don't do such things."

"Bullshit," Frank ranted as he went back to the stacks of volumes. He pulled two out and waved them at Ben. "Look at these. Grew at the Navy Court of Inquiry and then at the Army

Board; he was so suave, so composed. By God, Ben, he was well prepared and knew what he was doing. But then they nearly caught him. Look for yourself."

GREW

NAVY COURT OF INQUIRY

Present: All the members, the judge advocate and his council, the interested parties and their counsel, except Admiral Harold R. Stark, U.S. Navy, interested party, whose counsel were present.

No witnesses not otherwise connected with the inquiry were present.

(1062) A witness called by the court entered, was duly sworn and was informed of the subject matter of the inquiry.

Examined by the judge advocate:

1. Q. Will you state your name, residence, and present position?

A. Joseph Clark Grew: residence, Washington, D.C. My present position is Director of the Office of Far Eastern Affairs, Department of State.

2. Q. What position did you hold during the year 1941?

A. During 1941, up to December 7th, I was Ambassador to Japan.

Examined by the court:

3. Q. Mr. Ambassador, there is information before this court which alleges that on or about January 27, 1941, you transmitted information to our government that an attack would be made on Pearl Harbor. Is that correct, sir?

A. Admiral, the information which I then transmitted was in the nature of a rumor that had reached me but a rumor which came from sources which I considered reliable.

4. Q. Did these rumors persist? Did they continue, with special reference to an attack on Pearl Harbor?

A. So far as I can now recollect, that was the only occasion on which I received a definite intimation that there might be, in case of war or in case of a break between Japan and the United States, an attack on Pearl Harbor. I do not recollect other occasions on which Pearl Harbor was mentioned in that connection.

5. Q. Subsequent to this date, that is, January, 1941, and subsequent to this report which you made to the State Department, did you, prior to December 7, 1941, make a similar report as to a possible or probable attack on Pearl Harbor?

A. In the further reports which I made between January and December, 1941, I do not recollect that Pearl Harbor was actually mentioned, although I sent a number of reports warning our government that Japan might strike with dangerous and dramatic suddenness.

6. Q. Such a report as that was made by you on or about November 3rd?

A. Yes, sir.

7. Q. In making this report that Japan might strike with dramatic or dangerous suddenness, did you have in mind at that time the area or the position which she would strike with dramatic and dangerous suddenness?

A. No, sir. I did not, specifically, and in one of my reports to our government I stated that our government (1063) should not depend upon me to tell them where and when Japan might strike because I would not know, the Japanese being past masters at secrecy.

Cross-examined by the judge advocate:

30. Q. I have a document which is a letter from the Chief of Naval Operations to the Commander-in-Chief of the Pacific Fleet under date of February 1, 1941. It purports to quote information which, under date of 27 January 1941, the American Ambassador at Tokyo telegraphed the State Department. I would ask you to examine the quoted part of this document to see whether or not it contains the substance of a report that you, in fact, made?

A. That, in general, is the substance of my report, although it is really a paraphrase of the actual text. I think my memory has played me false here. I said before it was the Portuguese Minister as being the source of my information. It states here "the Peruvian Minister." I think that is accurate.

Cross-examined by the interested party, Admiral Harold R. Stark, U.S. Navy:

31. Q. Mr. Ambassador, going back to your dispatch of 27 January 1941 concerning the attack on Pearl Harbor. If you feel free to do so, will you elaborate upon your answer and give the source of the rumors and information which caused you to send that dispatch?

A. Yes, sir. The dispatch states: "A member of the Embassy was told by me"—this is a close paraphrase—"———— colleague that from many quarters, including a Japanese one, he had heard that a surprise mass attack on Pearl Harbor was planned by the Japanese military forces, in case of 'trouble' between Japan and the United States;" that source was the Peruvian Minister, a man in whom I had a considerable degree of confidence.

32. Q. Do you recall any other source that came to you (1067) with this information about that time or just previously, to the same effect?

A. I do not recall any specific source. My colleague said that he was prompted to pass this on because it had come to him from many sources, although the plan seemed fantastic. I do not now recollect that that precise report came to me from any other source.

33. Q. But as to that, you did give it a rather high evaluation in your own mind; is that correct, Mr. Ambassador?

A. That is a very difficult question to answer, Admiral, but I will say this: Although my Peruvian colleague labeled the report as fantastic, I still considered that it was of such utmost importance that I could not afford to regard it as fantastic, and for that reason I passed it on to the Secretary of State. I don't think I can go further than that in answering your question.

Ben put down the volume, shook his head, and looked at the Army Pearl Harbor Board Report. "Is this the same?" he asked.

Frank looked grimly at Ben. "Read it."

As Ben opened to the paper-clipped section, Frank asked, "You want coffee or a drink?"

"Coffee. I don't think I could handle a drink while reading this bullshit."

Frank went to the kitchen and Ben went back to reading.

⌐   ¬

Army Pearl Harbor Board

(4197)   TESTIMONY OF THE HONOR-
ABLE JOSEPH CLARK GREW,
FORMER AMBASSADOR TO JA-
PAN, DEPARTMENT OF STATE,
WASHINGTON, D.C.

(The Witness was sworn by the Recorder and advised of his rights under Article of War 24.)

1. COLONEL WEST. Mr. Grew, will you please state to the Board your name and address.

MR. GREW. Joseph Clark Grew; official address, Department of State; personal address, 2840 Woodland Drive, Washington.

2. GENERAL GRUNERT. Mr. Grew, the Board very much appreciates your coming over. We wanted to come over to see you, but I understand you insisted on coming to us, and we appreciate it very much.

MR. GREW. Very happy to!

3. GENERAL GRUNERT. In this particular part of our investigation I am going to ask General Russell to lead in asking the questions, and then, if the rest of the Board have anything to add, they will interrupt or add, afterward.

4. GENERAL RUSSELL. You were formerly our Ambassador to Japan?

MR. GREW. Yes, sir; I was.

5. GENERAL RUSSELL. Would you state for the purpose of the record just what period of time was covered in that activity?

MR. GREW. I was Ambassador to Japan, and I presented my credentials there on June 4, 1932. I functioned officially until December 7, 1941.

6. GENERAL RUSSELL. There was a very good reason for the termination of your services as Ambassador to Japan, on the 7th of December, 1941, was there, Mr. Grew?

MR. GREW. I would say, a compelling reason, General.

(4198) 7. GENERAL RUSSELL. During the period that you were out there as Ambassador to Japan, did you keep a diary of the events which you considered worthy of preserving?

MR. GREW. I did, sir.

8. GENERAL RUSSELL. Later, did you embody the contents of that diary in a book which you published?

MR. GREW. I did, sir—part of the contents.

9. GENERAL RUSSELL. It embodied only part of the contents?

MR. GREW. A very small part, because there was no room for the voluminous diary which I kept during those years.

10. GENERAL RUSSELL. Mr. Ambassador, is the book which I have in my hand, and which I now exhibit to you, entitled "Ten Years in Japan," the book which was authored by you, with your diary as the basis?

MR. GREW. It is, sir. It was based partly

on my diary and partly on my official dispatches and telegrams.

11. GENERAL RUSSELL. Your relation with Washington was through the office of the Secretary of State, largely?

MR. GREW. It was, sir.

13. GENERAL RUSSELL. When, in your opinion, did it become evident that war with Japan was inevitable?

MR. GREW. I could not put my finger on any particular date, General. My own position, there, was that I was going to fight up to the last possible minute to prevent war; and I did everything in my power to prevent it; and, not being a defeatist by nature, I was unwilling to admit that war was inevitable, up to the last minute. So that I cannot mention any particular date, prior to December 7, 1941, when I felt that war was definitely inevitable.

17. GENERAL RUSSELL. Mr. Ambassador, we have read your book, and we have made a study of the book "Peace and War" which was prepared under the supervision of the State Department, the most of which, as it relates to our dealings with Japan, is constructed around the information which you sent back from Japan. There are two or three things in this book which we want to impose on you for a minute to ask you about. (4203) There is a message of January 27, '41, which is the message that some conversation was occurring between the consulates in Japan in which the Japanese source had stated that in event of trouble with the United States a mass attack on Pearl Harbor was planned by the Japanese. We have won-

dered what the basis of that message might be.

MR. GREW. General, the basis of that message was a statement made to a member of my staff by the Peruvian Minister in Tokyo, a man in whom I had full confidence, on the basis of reports which he had heard from Japanese sources. I do not know the actual sources from which he received that report, by name, but they were such that he placed a certain amount of weight upon them: and, while in imparting this information to the member of my staff the Minister said he considered it a fantastic rumor, at the same time he felt that it was sufficiently important to justify his passing it on to me.

18. GENERAL RUSSELL. And the Peruvian Minister from whom you received the information was a man of such type and you attached importance to it to the extent that you forwarded that information to the Secretary of State?

MR. GREW. Yes, sir; he was a substantial man, a close personal friend of mine. I knew him very well, I had known him for years and I was quite certain that he would not mislead me in anything that he might pass on to me.

Frank was pouring himself a second cup of coffee from the heavy silver service he had brought from the kitchen.

"What do you think?" Frank asked.

"How'd they get away with it? Surely someone was there to feed them information?"

Frank nodded. "Right. Max Hamilton. He was designated to supply the documents. Hell it had

195

been worked perfectly. Remember, Ben, they had all the time in the world. Those hearings were not held until 1944, and nobody else had access to any department documents during that period. Hornbeck had pulled off one of the greatest political crimes in our history. He even did it with the innocent blessing of the Secretary. And they didn't waste any time getting at it. Look at the date of this, just nine days after the attack on Pearl Harbor."

DEPARTMENT OF STATE

ADVISOR ON POLITICAL RELATIONS

December 16, 1941.

Mr. Secretary:

We have arranged with Mr. Spaulding for him to take charge of and set three or four men to work upon compilation of documents in United States-Japanese relations for the period September 18, 1931 to December 7, 1941. Mr. Hamilton, Mr. Ballantine, Mr. Hiss and I will keep in close touch with this work as it proceeds. Mr. Ballantine will have special charge of the data relating to the exploratory conversations of this year.

S.K.H.

"But wouldn't the Secretary have some suspicions?" Stockton asked. "Hell, Frank, this is obvious as all get out."

Schuler had calmed down and his voice had moderated. "Think about when this all began. The Secretary had been duped, but he did not know it. He never suspected the devious minds of the men he had come to trust over the years. Also, you have to remember that he felt a very personal, very direct, sense of failure. After the Japs attacked, he was nearly a broken man. By the time the hearings—the Joint Committee Hearings—were underway, he was so ill that he could hardly make any appearances to testify. In addition to that, Max Hamilton and Ballantine were the ones who were feeding the source material to him. He was so ill that his memory was not alert enough to compensate for the altered documents. He testified in good faith, but, with FDR dead and new men running the Department, hell, he couldn't be held responsible. But, they nearly got Grew in the questioning. He handles himself well, but it was a close call for him. Look at this segment from the Joint Committee hearings."

As Ben finished the Army and Navy Reports, Frank offered one final page from the Joint Committee Hearings. Ben went back to reading.

The Chairman. Senator George.

Senator George. Nothing now, at this time.

The Chairman. Mr. Clark.

Mr. Clark. I want to ask you if you inquired from your diplomatic colleague the source of his information in regard to the attack on Pearl Harbor?

Mr. Grew. I do not think I did, Mr. Congressman. After all, sometimes when an official, diplomatic official receives information of that kind or even a rumor report of that kind, it may put him in a rather difficult

197

position to ask him to reveal the source. I do not think I did ask that question.

Mr. Clark. You did not ask him where he learned that there was likely to be an attack on Pearl Harbor?

Mr. Grew. What is that?

Mr. Clark. You did not ask him where he learned that there was likely to be an attack on Pearl Harbor?

Mr. Grew. I do not recollect having asked that question.

Mr. Clark. Well, now, I do not mean to insist upon this, but you considered it important enough to make it the subject of a special dispatch to your Government, did you not?

Mr. Grew. Definitely.

Mr. Clark. You say now you made no effort to find out the source from which he obtained that information?

(1507) Mr. Grew. To have gone to my Peruvian colleague and said, "I would like to know the source from which you received that information," would have put him in a very difficult position, because most of those pieces of information were received from Japanese friends who would have been endangered by the knowledge that they had passed that information on. I think in all probability if I had asked my colleague for the source he probably would have felt that he could not give it to me. In any case, it is a rather difficult thing to do, to ask for such a thing as that.

Mr. Clark. Did you know him pretty well?

Mr. Grew. I knew him pretty well. He was a man I trusted. I trusted his word and I trusted his judgment.

198

The Chairman. There is one question I omitted to ask, if I may do it now.

Mr. Grew. Yes.

The Chairman. In regard to this rumor brought to your attention by the Peruvian Minister or Ambassador.

Mr. Grew. Minister.

The Chairman. The testimony here shows that in January 1941, Admiral Yamamoto, I believe it is, the Japanese Admiral, had formulated some plan by which to attack Pearl Harbor at some indefinite date in the future. Would you be able to know whether the formulation of such plan by the Japanese Admiral might have had any connection with the rumors that the Peruvian Minister passed on to you?

Mr. Grew. I think that is very doubtful, Mr. Chairman. The Japanese were pretty effective in their secrecy. I think it is very unlikely that that information would have been allowed to leak out anywhere. It would have been probably retained in a very small group of the highest military and naval officers, so that I would doubt very much if the rumors which I telegraphed the Secretary of State on January 27 had any connection whatever with the elaborating of the plan.

Stockton stopped reading and shook his head in disbelief. "This is impossible. I met personally with Schreiber. He said that Grew insulted him with his attitude. Grew even told me he didn't want to be accused of crying wolf. Hell, Frank, the man lied to the Committee."

"You aren't telling me anything I don't know," Schuler said glumly.

He heard Ben Stockton behind him suddenly whoop with glee. "I've got it! His diary! The old bastard was such an egomaniac that it would be in his diary. If we told Senator Barkley about the diary then . . . ."

"They know about the diary."

"Then they must know . . . ."

Schuler cut him off. "He refused to let them see it. But it wouldn't do much good. He's already changed the damned thing."

Ben's eyes widened. "How do you know that?"

"Everybody knows it. Grew had great legal advice from his cohorts—like Jane Barton. I've talked to several other friends of mine still in the Department and they are sure that Jane was in on the deal. She probably gave Grew the advice he needed."

"Advice?" Ben choked. "What the hell legal advice did he need?"

"First he refused to let them see the diary," Frank said. "Then they found out that the text had been altered."

"Who found out?"

"The Committee. They knew that he had changed the diary, but Grew was on firm legal ground and he simply assumed a posture of privileged privacy and that was that."

"But if they knew about the changes in the diary . . . ."

Schuler cut him off again by tossing another volume of the Congressional Report at him. "Hell, read it yourself."

DIARY

PROCEEDINGS OF JOINT COMMITTEE

Senator Ferguson. Does the committee have a copy of your (1636) diary?

Mr. Grew. No, sir; the diary was a purely personal and private document. The important parts of my diary are published in my book, what I call the highlights.

Senator Ferguson. Do I understand, Mr. Grew, the committee does not have access—I am talking about counsel for the committee—does not have access to your diary to determine what might be important to this committee?

Mr. Grew. Senator, I would like to have the record straight on this, if you will permit me.

Senator Ferguson. I wish you would make the record straight.

Mr. Grew. I will read a copy of my letter to Mr. Mitchell, the General Counsel.

Senator Ferguson. You may read it.

Mr. Grew. This is dated November 12, 1945.

(Grew reads letter saying diary is not an official document and his own private property.)

Senator Ferguson. Now do I understand that you submitted your diary to the State Department to determine what you might put in this book Ten Years in Japan?

Mr. Grew. That is always done, Senator,

especially in wartime. That, to my recollection is done in every case.

Senator Ferguson. That was not my question. My question was: Did you submit it to the State Department?

Mr. Grew. I submitted the manuscript of my book.

Senator Ferguson. Did they take anything out?

Mr. Grew. I do not think they made an actual demand, but they suggested that certain passages might be eliminated; some of them because they could have caused embarrassment or actual danger to individuals, sometimes, where they might have been misinterpreted by the foreign governments, and points of that kind.

Frankly, after receiving the suggestions of the Publications Committee in the Department of State I found myself in entire accord with it. There is nothing that I reluctantly withdrew.

(1642) Senator Ferguson. Do you think your diary may have helped counsel to obtain from the files, which I understand are very voluminous, some of the important documents? For instance, this document?

Mr. Grew. I do not think so, Senator. I think, as I say, the high lights of the correspondence appear in my diary and then the running comment from day to day of what I was thinking at the time. I think the diary would not be an appropriate document in this investigation, and I would like to explain why, if I may.

Senator Ferguson. I wish you would.

Mr. Grew. You will find in my book, on

202

page 348, under date of November 1, 1940, I made the following entry in my diary:

In the light of fast-moving developments I scarcely dare read back in the diary nowadays because of its many inconsistencies which show it up for the patchwork sort of day-to-day scribbling it is. At least it shows our thoughts and our information, some of it reliable and some of it wholly unreliable, at any given moment—the moment of writing. It shows how often we are groping and fumbling in the dark. Less and less are we able to know what is going on behind the scenes, simply because many of our reliable contacts are no longer available and (1643) also because, even behind the scenes, the right hand often doesn't know what the left hand is doing.

Senator Ferguson. Of course, when you were referring there to "we," you were talking about the Embassy in Tokyo?

Mr. Grew. Yes, sir; I was.

Senator Ferguson. Mr. Grew, did you give your diary to the State Department when they checked your manuscript for your book?

Mr. Grew. No sir; I did not.

Senator Ferguson. Do you have the parts that the State Department deleted from your book?

(1842) Mr. Grew. I had them at the time, yes.

Senator Ferguson. Do you have them now?

Mr. Grew. A good many of them were deleted by me myself, because when I prepared the original manuscript it is always easier to prepare too much rather than too little material, and many passages were already marked "cut" before they were handed to the State Department at all. I do not have that manuscript now. I sent it to my publishers at the time, nearly two years ago now, and I suppose it has been destroyed.

Senator Ferguson. You do not have anything then that would give us what was cut out or deleted by the State Department?

Mr. Grew. No sir, I could not. I am not trying to conceal anything. I am trying to give every possible piece of information which will be helpful to this committee.

I also said in my letter that I have gone through the last several months in my diary before Pearl Harbor very carefully to see if I could find anything that might be pertinent to this hearing and, frankly, I found nothing.

That is my position, Mr. Chairman.

The Chairman. All right. Senator Ferguson.

Senator Ferguson. Mr. Grew, you do feel, however, that your position does place in you the determination as to what is material or not material to this inquiry?

Mr. Grew. Senator, as I have said constantly, after all, the controlling factor in all of these matters is the official correspondence. The official correspondence, everything that passed between the Department of State and myself is on the record here on file, and, as Mr. Mitchell said, available to the committee.

Now, the material on which those official reports were based, I don't think would be helpful to the committee.

Senator Ferguson. But it does place in you, in you solely, that determination, the attitude that you take; isn't that true?

Mr. Grew. That is a question of interpretation, possibly (1853) legal interpretation, and I don't believe I would want to try to answer the question as to whether any man has a right to retain his personal and private documents, that is a legal matter I couldn't answer.

Senator Ferguson. I have just a few more questions.

Was it your custom to make over-all reports to the Secretary of State or the President, for instance, when you returned in 1939 to the United States to make a report to the President?

Mr. Grew. Well, of course, Senator, whenever I came back on leave of absence from my post, I saw the President and had a talk with him and saw the Secretary of State and had a talk with him, and naturally in those talks I painted the picture as I saw it at that time. I did not, I am afraid, keep records of those talks. When I came back I was in Washington only a short time and kept no records of those talks.

Senator Ferguson. Do you know whether or not the Secretary of State kept records of those talks?

Mr. Grew. That I do not know.

Senator Ferguson. Would counsel inquire if he did?

Mr. Grew, it was customary then to make over-all reports when you finally returned after the war had started? I think you returned—in what year?

(1854) Mr. Grew. I returned on August 25, 1942.

Senator Ferguson. Did you report to Mr. Hull at that time?

Mr. Grew. Yes, I did.

Senator Ferguson. Did you report in writing?

Mr. Grew. Everything had been written pretty well up to date.

Senator Ferguson. That isn't quite my question.

Mr. Grew. No; I don't recollect having submitted at that time any reports in writing.

Senator Ferguson. Will you think about that? That could be an important report.

Mr. Keefe. Well now, when you came back finally from Japan you brought with you a diary consisting, as I understand (1932) it, of some 13 volumes; is that right?

Mr. Grew. I believe that is correct, Mr. Congressman.

Mr. Keefe. And that is the diary which has been the subject of some discussion between you and the committee and Senator Brewster?

Mr. Grew. That is correct.

Mr. Keefe. Now, Mr. Grew, after you came back with this diary of 13 volumes, will you state whether or not you submitted it to Collier's weekly for publication; for publication by Collier's weekly first?

Mr. Grew. I did not submit the entire diary to Collier's weekly. I did submit parts of it having in mind the possibility of a series of articles but I later found that I could not write that series of articles and the whole thing was dropped.

Mr. Keefe. Now, as a matter of fact—and you can answer this or not, as you wish, Mr. Grew—isn't it a fact that you did submit your diary to Collier's weekly for the purpose of having it edited into a series of articles and that when it was submitted it was found that there had been passages cut out of the diary and Collier's weekly was not interested in publishing the diary with those deleted portions taken out?

Mr. Grew. I don't recollect that. The whole diary was not submitted.

(1933) Mr. Keefe. What part was submitted?

Mr. Grew. I can't recollect. Certain parts were submitted to one representative of Collier's weekly to look over and see whether a series of articles would be worth while.

Mr. Keefe. Who was that man?

Mr. Grew. I can't recollect his name now. He is now dead. I think he died last year. But I can't remember his name.

Mr. Keefe. Was he not the Washington representative of Collier's weekly, the man to whom you submitted the diary?

Mr. Grew. I don't think so.

The Chairman. I was trying to think of his name. I think I knew him.

Mr. Grew. I remember that he came down to meet me when we got off the Japanese ship to see if he could sign me up for a series of articles. I wasn't willing to sign up at that time but as he had taken the trouble I realized that if I was going to write anything for the magazines that Collier's weekly had a reasonable priority. We looked over the ground and I finally decided that I did not want to write those articles at that time and the whole thing was dropped.

Mr. Keefe. Where were those conversations held, here in Washington?

Mr. Grew. Well—the talks about the diary?

(1934) Mr. Keefe. Yes.

Mr. Grew. I think so.

Mr. Keefe. What volumes of your diary did you submit to him?

Mr. Grew. I couldn't possibly tell you, Mr. Congressman. I wouldn't remember.

Mr. Keefe. Do you wish to say that Collier's weekly categorically did or did not refuse to publish an article because of the deletions which appeared in your diary?

Mr. Grew. I don't recollect any such decision now.

Mr. Keefe. Well, would you say that that decision was not reached or that you just do not remember?

Mr. Grew. I haven't thought of that incident. It is at least 3 years ago now. As far as I can recollect the matter, Collier's never abandoned the idea completely. I think I just didn't go ahead with it. I don't recollect that Collier's definitely declined to publish. No, I don't recollect that.

Mr. Keefe. Will you answer this question, please:

Was it your intention to personally write the diary or did Collier's suggest that you go over it with an editorial writer that would shape up the material.

Mr. Grew. I think the idea was that certain parts could be taken out and possibly an editorial writer might go over (1935) them and write up something for me.

Mr. Keefe. Did you discuss the matter with any editorial writer of Collier's weekly?

Mr. Grew. Only in a very general way. We never got down to details.

Mr. Keefe. What editorial writer of Collier's did you discuss the matter with?

Mr. Grew. That was that gentleman whose name escapes me. I can't recollect it. I believe he died last year. I can't remember his name.

Mr. Keefe. What specific reason do you now ascribe for failing to go on and having Collier's publish the diary?

Mr. Grew. Well, I can't remember exactly the reasons. In the first place, I was exceedingly busy. I was making speeches all over the country. And I dare say that at that time I possibly was thinking of a book, in which case it would have been better not to do a series of articles. I think that was the idea, that I was proposing to bring out this book and therefore that I did not wish to go ahead with the articles.

Mr. Keefe. How many volumes of your diary did you turn over to Collier's to inspect?

Mr. Grew. I don't remember whether I turned over the actual volumes or not. I had copies of various parts of the (1936) diary which I think I showed them. Whether I showed them the volumes or not I don't know.

.1937) Mr. Keefe. You just do not recall?

Mr. Grew. No, sir.

Mr. Keefe. Well, then, after you decided, or it was decided, whatever the fact may be, that you were not going to have Collier's publish this series of articles to whom did you next submit your material for publication?

Mr. Grew. To whom did I next submit my material for publication?

Mr. Keefe. Yes.

Mr. Grew. I then decided to go ahead with the book and I decided to put it in the hands of Messrs. Simon and Schuster of New York and Mr. Quincy Howe, one of their foremost editors whom I knew personally, went over the diary with me and helped me pick—

Mr. Keefe. Now, you submitted your complete diary to Mr. Quincy Howe, did you not?

Mr. Grew. At one time he had it, yes.

Mr. Keefe. Yes. And he went through it for the purpose of editing this book, did he not?

Mr. Grew. That is correct.

Mr. Keefe. And he prepared the material that went into this book, Ten Years in Japan?

Mr. Grew. No, he did not prepare it.

Mr. Keefe. Well he put it together?

Mr. Grew. Well, he made suggestions as to passages that might be used and it was up to me to decide whether they should be used or not. In the last analysis I had this considerable amount of material and I decided what I wanted published and what was published.

Mr. Keefe. Well, you supervised it, Mr. Grew, I think.

Mr. Grew. That is correct.

Mr. Keefe. He actually drew up a manuscript, did he not?

Mr. Grew. That is correct.

Mr. Keefe. That is, under your supervision?

Mr. Grew. That is correct.

Mr. Keefe. And before publication could be had of that manuscript it had to be taken down to the State Department and cleared there, did it not?

Mr. Grew. As I said the other day, Mr. Congressman, in wartime everything which is published by an officer of the Government is supposed to be considered by a publication committee which then existed in the Department of State.

Mr. Keefe. Yes. Well, I understand that, of course. It is a simple question. It was submitted, regardless of reason, to the State Department?

Mr. Grew. That is a fact.

Mr. Keefe. And the reason was that we were at war and (1939) they had a right to see what was being published.

Mr. Grew. That is a fact.

Mr. Keefe. Now, then, when this original manuscript was prepared by Mr. Howe as the editor in charge of this, working for you and for Simon & Schuster, it was submitted to the State Department and there were suggestions for deletions from this manuscript, were there not?

Mr. Grew. There were.

Mr. Keefe. And a new manuscript was prepared with the deletions?

Mr. Grew. I do not remember whether a new manuscript was prepared or whether the original manuscript was simply clipped. I dare say that the original manuscript was clipped of the passages which I determined to cut out and that manuscript was sent back to the publishers.

Mr. Keefe. Do you remember what the deletions were about?

Mr. Grew. Well, as I said the other day, they were about a variety of things. Some of the deletions were taken out at my own initiative because I had prepared more material than could be comprised in the kind of book that my publishers wished to bring out. Therefore, that material had to be materially cut down.

In fact, when the original manuscripts were prepared there were a good many passages in there marked "cut", to be (1940) considered as to whether there was room for them or not and, if so, whether they would fit in with the type of book I was going to publish. A good many of those passages I cut out myself.

It was suggested by the committee, and I remember no demand on their part at all, but suggested that certain passages might well be omitted because they might embarrass or possibly even injure or endanger individuals during wartime, that they might be misinterpreted by foreign governments, passages of all kinds of natures which were cut out for one reason or another, but mostly of that kind.

Mr. Keefe. Do you remember, Mr. Grew, that after the second revision of this manuscript had been prepared that the story of the death march on Bataan was published in this country?

Mr. Grew. Well, I do not recollect the precise chronology of that. I remember very well that the story on the death march in Bataan was published in this country.

Mr. Keefe. And didn't the publication of that story precipitate the necessity for further revision of your manuscript and wasn't it revised after that story was published?

Mr. Grew. Not to my recollection whatsoever. I do not think that that had anything whatsoever to do with it.

Mr. Keefe. Well, do you want to state categorically that (1941) it did not have anything to do with it?

Mr. Grew. No.

Mr. Keefe. Or that you just do not remember?

Mr. Grew. I frankly do not remember.

Mr. Keefe. All right.

Mr. Grew. I do not believe it had anything to do with it.

Mr. Keefe. I thought he said he had finished. Had you finished?

Mr. Grew. I finished, sir, yes.

Mr. Keefe. Yes. Well, in order to prepare this book under those circumstances it was necessary at least for Mr. Quincy Howe to have the benefit of reading your entire diary, was it not?

Mr. Grew. He had the benefit of reading the diary; yes, sir.

Mr. Keefe. And he is a reputable man, is he not?

Mr. Grew. He is a completely reputable man.

Mr. Keefe. And you would believe him, would you not?

Mr. Grew. I certainly would, otherwise I certainly would not have entrusted the diary to him.

Mr. Keefe. Now, do you know how many other people in the office of Simon & Schuster had access to your diary besides Mr. Quincy Howe?

(1942) Mr. Grew. I doubt very much if anybody did.

Mr. Keefe. Well, he was up in New York, wasn't he?

Mr. Grew. Mr. Howe was in New York, yes.

Mr. Keefe. And the diary was with him?

Mr. Grew. That is right.

Mr. Keefe. And you were here in Washington and out on the road making speeches?

Mr. Grew. That is perfectly correct.

Mr. Keefe. Now, you cannot say how many people could have had access to this diary then, can you?

Mr. Grew. Well, I cannot tell you categorically but I know that Mr. Quincy Howe is a man of such reputability that he would not have for a moment left the diary in a position where other people could have access to it.

Mr. Keefe. Well, would you have any objections to Mr. Howe testifying here as a witness as to the material that was cut out of this manuscript?

Mr. Grew. Well, that comes right down, I think, to the question originally brought up as to whether I am not within my rights in claiming that the diary itself was of a personal and private nature; that I have produced in my book the pertinent material which I think would be helpful to this committee; that I have looked through the diary for the months preceding Pearl Harbor and have found nothing further that I (1943) think would be pertinent to this committee.

The question arises on that basis if I am not justified in regarding the rest of the diary as a personal and private document. I feel very strongly on that point myself.

The Chairman. Well, the Chair might suggest that regardless of Mr. Grew's attitude or his willingness or unwillingness for Mr. Quincy Howe to testify about this personal diary, it may be a matter, after all, for the committee to determine whether it would call Mr. Howe to testify about that.

Mr. Grew. Undoubtedly it would be, Mr. Chairman, yes.

Mr. Murphy. Mr. Chairman, may I inquire of the gentleman from Wisconsin if he feels that Mr. Quincy Howe would shed any light on the Pearl Harbor investigation and whether we should call him as a witness?

Mr. Keefe. Now, Mr. Chairman, I object to those kinds of interjections. I am acting in good faith.

The Chairman. The Chair hopes that the committee will not get into a discussion over Mr. Quincy Howe at this stage of the proceedings, so go ahead, Congressman, with your inquiry.

"Frank," Stockton said with anger in his voice, "this is criminal."

Schuler poured more coffee. "You think this is bad? You should read the whole thing. It would make you sick. The final analysis is that the military was wrong, FDR was wrong, the whole damned nation was wrong. The only people who were right were those bastards Grew and Hornbeck and their bunch. Don't you realize, Ben. Joe Grew looks like a damned hero in this. A bloody national hero who was a prophet to boot. I don't know if the whole story will ever come out. From what I have learned, Ballantine and the others changed, actually retyped, hundreds of documents and they misfiled or destroyed others. It would be nearly impossible to ever dig up the proof."

"Will you do it?" Stockton asked.

Frank shook his head. "No, Ben. That's not my way of doing business. One simply does not go around accusing people in high positions in the Department. That's the job of the Congress or the White House. If Roosevelt had lived, things would have been different. I know he would have gotten Grew; he really hated that man for what he had done. If FDR were alive, then Grew and the others would be on the griddle."

"But why does that make a difference," Stockton asked. "What is the difference?"

"Because there is a whole new ball game. We have a new President, we have a new foreign policy, we have a new national purpose. I heard from an old Navy friend of mine that FDR met with Admirals King, Nimitz, and Halsey. There was a move to simply beat Japan, then blockade her and let her sink into the Pacific. I think FDR was sorely tempted to let that happen. But there is a new attitude in the world. We are going to start rebuilding Japan. That's why you and I are going to try and help MacArthur's Occupation Government. The decision has been made to help them get back onto their feet, so they can become a strong ally for us in the Far East. That is the irony."

"I don't understand."

Schuler did. He explained, "The tricks of Fate, Ben. Don't you see it? By accident Hornbeck, Grew, Hamilton, and the others took the attitude that there was a small militarist clique who pushed Japan into the war with us. They changed documents, altered reports, and made it look like they had been working with the pacifists in Japan. Hell, Grew spoke in his diary about the wonderful friendship he had with Prince Konoye, the Prime Minister just before Tojo. Of course, before the Joint Committee Hearings, he changed his tune. 'You sometimes had a civilian Prime Minister,' he told them, 'such as the first two ministries of Prince Konoye, in which the worst acts of international banditry in all history probably were carried out. That was the Jap that Grew wrote to and said, 'With expressions of my highest respect and cordial personal regards, I am, my dear Prince Konoye, Sincerely yours.' The body of the letter is worse. So you see, Ben, times and conditions change and it happened that Grew got lucky on this one."

"But the War Crimes Trials," Ben argued. "All of that will come out then."

"Sure it will. It will be proven that there was a small clique of militarists who gained unsupported control of the government and forced Japan into the war. A few heads will roll, but the Emperor will come out smelling like one of his roses, and there will be a whole bunch of 'former' politicians

217

who will become the new leaders of our new Japan."

"But there was no peace faction," said Stockton. "They all wanted war."

Frank agreed. "Sure, if the truth were known, then the people of the United States would demand that the Emperor swing from a rope and more along with him. If all of the people in Japan who wanted war were hanged for the crime of attacking without declaring war, then there would be very few people left in their Empire. Hell, we know now that the attack was no secret to the Japs; they were ready for it to happen and were elated when the story was finally made public. As for the Emperor, he was in it up to his neck."

Ben recalled his experiences in the Office of War Information in 1942, when attacks on the Emperor had been forbidden. He told Schuler about it.

"I doubt if Grew and the others knew about it, really," Schuler guessed. "I think they were just trying to save their asses and they did a magnificent job of it, too. Oh, it is known by the powers that be, and Grew and the others will get theirs in a quiet way; but it doesn't seem fair does it?"

"Hell, no, Frank, we should do some . . ." The front door opened; Olive had returned from her "shopping" trip.

"Well, Ben Stockton," she said, "how have you been?"

They shook hands as he said, "Fine, Olive. I've just been hearing a most incredible story."

Olive corrected him. "Not 'incredible', Ben. Horrible, yes; dastardly, yes; but not incredible. We know it happened."

"We should do something."

"Not now, Ben," said Frank. "The time is not right. We are in a time where some things are more important."

"We have our lives and that is important," said Olive. "Maybe someday we will be able to tell the story."

Frank Schuler looked out again at the nation's capital. "It'll come out, it has to."

POSTSCRIPT

Frank Schuler and his family's life and trial did not simply blend quietly into the fabric of history. Through the years he tried desperately to do two things. The first was to prove that he had been unjustly treated by the Department of State simply because he had been bright enough and man enough to challenge the limited minds of men like Joseph Grew and Stanley Hornbeck. The second was to try and make people see the truth about the Pearl Harbor debacle.

Both of his endeavors were thwarted by circumstances of the times and also by a hidden force still entrenched within the Department of State.

He would fight and work diligently to try and force some stability into his own diplomatic career but, when it was most unexpected, some totally unanticipated incident would crash into his life causing turmoil for him and his family.

From his own recollections, Frank tells of one terrible incident.

"It was, in February of 1953, in the heat of the McCarthy hearings on the State Department files, that my name suddenly sprang up in the headlines during the questioning of Helen Balog, a file clerk in the State Department.

Mr. Cohn. I want to call your attention particularly to a file concerning which this committee had some information, and that is a file of a Foreign Service officer named Schuler.

Mrs. Balog. Mr. Schuler is not a Foreign Service officer. He is a Foreign Service Staff officer.

Mr. Cohn. He is at the present time a Foreign Service Staff officer; is that correct?

Mrs. Balog. That is correct.

The Chairman. He is in HICOG, High Commissioner of Germany?

Mrs. Balog. I think he is in Paris now.

Mr. Cohn. Is he in Intelligence in Paris?

Mrs. Balog. I don't know. I don't know what his title is.

The Chairman. Do I understand that this man has been transferred from HICOG to Intelligence?

Mr. Cohn. That is information that we have, but we have not been able to verify it at this time. Apparently the witness does not have direct knowledge.

You do not know what duties he is performing in Paris?

Mrs. Balog. No.

Mr. Cohn. By the way, is this the Frank Schuler who was at one time discharged from the State Department for having left his post without authorization?

The Chairman. She might not know that.

Mrs. Balog. Well, he was terminated as an FSO.

Mr. Cohn. Now, are you familiar with the file of this Frank Schuler? Have you had occasion to examine that file?

Mrs. Balog. Yes: I was the one who had to revise it, because he has had so many files to merge that it was too big a job to give to those busy clerks, and one day I myself set the file up.

The Chairman. May I say, Mr. Counsel, that these witnesses, most of them, or some of them, have been cooperative and willing to give us all the information they could. I understand the Truman blackout order is still in existence. I understand the position of the Department is that they must follow that order until it is revoked by the new President. I would suggest that you be very careful not to ask these witnesses to violate even that order, which I consider an extremely bad order. But I think they are bound by it. In discussing the files, I think we should protect the witnesses.

Mr. Cohn. Very well, Mr. Chairman, we will keep that in mind.

The Chairman. I may say that I hope that order is revoked shortly.

Mr. Cohn. You say you had the job of revising this Frank Schuler's file; is that correct?

Mrs. Balog. Yes, sir.

Mr. Cohn. While you were engaged in that job of revising the file, did you go through the contents of the file?

Mrs. Balog. Of course. I had to.

Mr. Cohn. Was there a particular letter in that file at the time you went through it that you saw and that made some impression on you?

Mrs. Balog. Yes, sir.

Mr. Cohn. One particular letter; is that right?

Mrs. Balog. Yes, sir.

Mr. Cohn. Now, after your revision of the file, and after you put it back in its place, did that Frank Schuler file ever come to your attention at another time, at a later date?

Mrs. Balog. The confidential FSO storage file which we could not merge with his staff file, it was maintained in the storage confidential room, it came to my attention again.

Mr. Cohn. What were the circumstances of this Schuler confidential file coming to your attention at a later date?

Mrs. Balog. Someone came over there to ask to review the file; an agent.

Mr. Cohn. An agent of a security agency of the United States?

Mrs. Balog. Yes, sir.

Mr. Cohn. Was that an FBI agent?

Mrs. Balog. Yes, sir.

Mr. Cohn. He came over to review the Schuler file?

Mrs. Balog. That is right. And it was one of those old, unrevised files, where material is just dumped loose in the folder, and I dropped the thing. He had another file to review, and I asked him to let me get that material arranged for him in chronological date order before he started to review it. And then, having another file to review, he was agreeable.

The Chairman. You said you dropped the file?

Mrs. Balog. Yes, sir; I did. And it spilled all over the floor.

The Chairman. So, you wanted to put it together before he examined it?

Mrs. Balog. That is right.

Mr. Cohn. So, while he was looking at some other file, you put the material in the Schuler file back in order; is that right?

Mrs. Balog. That is right.

Mr. Cohn. While you were putting that material back in order, did you look to see whether or not this particular letter which had made an impression on you was still in the file?

Mrs. Balog. Frankly, I noticed that it was missing.

Mr. Cohn. You noticed that that letter was missing; is that right?

Mrs. Balog. Right.

Mr. Cohn. Did you make a careful examination of the file to make sure that the letter was not there?

Mrs. Balog. Yes; I went through it again.

Mr. Cohn. Did the FBI agent look at the file, too?

Mrs. Balog. Yes; he did.

Mr. Cohn. And neither of you could find that letter; is that right?

Mrs. Balog. Right.

Mr. Cohn. Was that letter a letter of recommendation for Schuler?

Mrs. Balog. Yes, sir.

Mr. Cohn. And by whom was that missing letter signed?

Mrs. Balog. Owen Lattimore.

"This sensational development was reported in the press all over the country, with banner headlines carrying the incriminating accusation— 'Letter of Recommendation from Owen Lattimore Mysteriously Missing from file of Foreign Service Officer.' This story was carried widely on TV as well as radio, and we learned of it via the Paris edition of the *New York Herald Tribune*.

"At the time the story broke I tried in vain in Paris to reach friends and superiors in the State Department, as well as officials in the Embassy in Paris. No one would see me, nor talk to me. I asked to come to Washington to appear at a hearing to defend the charge, but was given no opportunity to do so. In the meantime, I was attempting to find out whether such a letter existed as I had no previous knowledge of any letter from Owen Lattimore. Finally, I called the Assistant High Commissioner in Bonn, Germany, from which post I had been assigned to Paris. He was a personal friend and told me he would check the file and call me back. A half-hour later, he called to say there was a letter in my file, signed by Lattimore when he worked with the Office of War Information. This letter was merely a request for Japanese language experts to be placed on loan to the OWI on Japanese propaganda warfare matters. My name was one of a number on the list! It was not a letter of recommendation. Unknowingly, I had carried the allegedly missing letter along with me in my personnel file, which had been handed to me with a seal and marked "Confidential and Secret" to give to the personnel people in Frankfurt as a back-up information file. At that time an individual had no right to see his personnel file; and perhaps this has not changed. In any event, it is meaningless in that if certain papers are intended to be kept secret from an individual, there are many ways to accomplish this.

"My wife and I suffered through the ensuing weeks like two people awaiting a life sentence and completely in the dark as to what was going on. There was a complete lack of communication, and the reluctance of everyone to have any contact with us produced an overwhelming feeling of foreboding and impending disaster.

"Meanwhile I was carrying on my duties. But the blow finally came on April 15, 1953—my birthday. I was in Lisbon, Portugal, on an assignment. My wife received a phone call from a man in the Embassy's personnel office inquiring as to my whereabouts and my expected return time. She told him I was in Lisbon and due to return the upcoming Saturday. His message was short and ominous: "Tell him it is extremely urgent that he call me the minute he arrives, whether it be day or night." He left both his office and home phone numbers. My wife knew immediately that this was not good news. She phoned a close friend, the wife of the Commercial Attaché, expressing her fears, and it was decided that our two elder sons, 9 and 10 years of age, would leave Saturday morning to spend the weekend with the Attaché's family. It later turned out that she and her husband were aware of what was in store for us, but she didn't have the courage to tell my wife.

"I arrived from Lisbon on Saturday afternoon. Olive gave me the "urgent" message. I dialed the number nervously. A man whom I did not know answered and I said, 'This is Frank Schuler. I understand from my wife that you wanted me to call you.'

" 'Yes, Mr. Schuler,' he replied. 'You have been reduced-in-force [another way of saying you were fired] and have one month in which to pack and depart for the United States.' Then he hung up.

"I sat down, speechless. Olive asked what he had said, and when I told her, it was really only a confirmation of what she feared. She went into shock. She was pregnant, expecting our fourth child in three weeks. Though I attempted to console and reassure her, I knew she knew what was in store for us. We had seen this happen to too many others not to realize the tragedy this brought to each man and his family. Some had committed suicide.

"Her first thought was what to do about the baby that was due shortly. She called her doctor and arranged to see him Monday morning. He was French and Olive approached him very directly with the request that labor be induced. He protested; he had to have an explanation. Olive was reluctant to tell him; she was already subconsciously concealing the fact that we were victims of McCarthyism. However, the doctor insisted he would do nothing unless he had the reason, adding that it must be very compelling as he had never seen her distraught before. Olive told him. He became indignant, not at her, but at the entire situation, stating that the American people were so blind. They had helped save Europe from a monster, Hitler, and now they did not recognize

226

that they had their own monster. He agreed to induce delivery the next day.

"It was a girl—we loved our boys, but we had prayed that this baby would be a girl. And our prayers had been answered. She had ten fingers and ten toes and was in perfect health, and she was beautiful. Thank God. Somehow, we hoped this was a good omen. Upon her arrival at home three days later, each of the boys was permitted to sit in a large chair and hold her for a few minutes. They were so delighted. We were a close family; our children were the most important part of our life together.

"An ironic aftermath of our being ousted from the State Department transpired during the five day journey back to the United States on the S.S. *United States*.

"We sat at the same table for the entire journey which was customary as all tables were assigned. Our three sons were having the time of their lives as they were free to select anything and as much as they wanted from the menu. Being gourmets of a sort, they experimented with all the exciting dishes recommended to them by the waiter, who was jolly and enjoyed playing the game with them. On the last day, the waiter came to me and said that an elderly couple who had observed us throughout the voyage had asked him who we were. He had told them we were 'diplomats from the State Department.' The lady wanted to know if she could come to our table with her husband and meet us.

" 'Of course,' we said. 'We would be honored and delighted.'

"After introducing themselves, and telling us they were from the mid-West, the lady said, 'My husband and I have admired you and your family so much throughout this voyage, and we just want you to know that we are so proud to know that it is people like you who represent our country abroad. If you and your family are an example of State Department families, we are now reassured. From what we have been reading in the newspapers we have been very concerned as to what kind of people the State Department had to represent us abroad.' We thanked them. Olive was so touched that she started to cry and excused herself and rushed out of the dining room. Little did they know that we were not sleeping nights. Olive was in a somewhat shaken state, having just had a new baby and come home and started to pack, and was spending her nights in tears. It was a very emotional time. However, I must say here, that upon arrival in the U.S. and after some time for taking hold of the situation, she proceeded with the task with great might and courage and endurance. We had much work to do to keep our family together.

"The Foreign Service had finally dealt the fatal blow. I was finished! They no longer needed to be concerned as to where I was being assigned."

The intellect which could give life to what we now include in our vernacular as "Watergate" came as no surprise to Olive and Frank Schuler. They *lived* the experience long before anyone could conceive of such happenings.

But Frank's integrity was a driving force that guided his life. That integrity was such that he kept the story buried painfully within himself because of his loyalty to the Department of State. That same integrity, when times and conditions had changed, motivated him to begin to make known a vital piece of history. Frank Schuler does not see himself as someone apart, someone odd in the historical chronicle of the Department of State; he knows there were others who had been unjustly treated. But he has a compulsion that is driving him now and that force is two pronged: He wants his fellow countrymen to know the truth of Pearl Harbor and he wants to bring the Department of State to task for their unfair and damaging treatment of him over the years.

In his personal papers, Frank has one document in particular that has been the straw to which he has clung all these years. Yes, The Freedom of Information Act helped, the Watergate exposé helped, and the support of his family helped more than anything, but that small scrap of paper, an AP wire story clipping from the Washington *Post* on July 22, 1946, has been a source of inspiration for more than thirty years.

From the Washington *Post*—22 July 1946
PEARL HARBOR FACTS NOT IN, FERGUSON SAYS
Michigan Senator Hopes Diplomats
Will Furnish Story
By the Associated Press

Senator Ferguson (R., Mich.) said yesterday the State Department should supplement Congress' Pearl Harbor report with "diplomatic facts."

Ferguson said he was sure the joint committee which reported its findings on the December 7, 1941, debacle last night did not get all the information to which the public is entitled about international negotiations bearing on the inquiry.

But the Michigan Republican said the six-month-long hearing went as far as a congressional committee could go. He foresaw no attempt to reopen it now or in the near future, he told a reporter.

(Ferguson had signed a minority report differing with the majority on who was to blame.)

The minority report, also signed by Senator Brewster, (R., Me.) contended that "the whole question of whether or not it would have been possible to avoid war by proper diplomatic action and thus avert the Pearl Harbor tragedy was left largely unexplored."

"We did not want the people and historians to believe we had all the facts," Ferguson said.

APPENDIX A

PRIOR INVESTIGATIONS CONCERNING PEARL HARBOR ATTACK

The Roberts Commission

The Roberts Commission was organized under an Executive order, dated December 18, 1941, of President Franklin D. Roosevelt, which defined the duties of the Commission thus: "To ascertain and report the facts relating to the attack made by Japanese armed forces upon the Territory of Hawaii on December 7, 1941. The purpose of the required inquiry and report are to provide bases for sound decisions whether any derelictions of duty or errors of judgment on the part of United States Army or Navy personnel contributed to such successes as were achieved by the enemy on the occasion mentioned; and, if so, what these derelictions or errors were, and who were responsible therefore." This inquiry was commenced on December 18, 1941, and was concluded on January 23, 1942. The record of its proceedings and exhibits covers 2,173 printed pages. Members of the Commission were Mr. Justice Owen J. Roberts, United States Supreme Court, Chairman; Admiral William H. Standley, United States Navy, retired; Rear Adm. Joseph M.

Reeves, United States Navy, retired; Maj. Gen. Frank R. McCoy, United States Army, retired; and Brig. Gen. Joseph T. McNarney, United States Army.

The Hart Inquiry

The inquiry conducted by Admiral Thomas C. Hart, United States Navy, retired, was initiated by precept dated February 12, 1944, from Secretary of the Navy Frank Knox to Admiral Hart "For an Examination of Witnesses and the Taking of Testimony Pertinent to the Japanese Attack on Pearl Harbor, Territory of Hawaii." The precept states ". . . Whereas certain members of the naval forces, who have knowledge pertinent to the foregoing matters, are now or soon may be on dangerous assignments at great distances from the United States . . . it is now deemed necessary, in order to prevent evidence being lost by death or unavoidable absence of those certain members of the naval forces, that their testimony, pertinent to the aforesaid Japanese attack, be recorded and preserved. . . ." This inquiry was commenced on February 12, 1944, and was concluded on June 15, 1944. The record of its proceedings and exhibits covers 565 printed pages.

The Army Pearl Harbor Board

The Army Pearl Harbor Board was appointed pursuant to the provisions of Public Law 332, Seventy-Eighth Congress, approved June 13, 1944, and by order dated July 8, 1944, of The Adjutant General, War Department. The board was directed "to ascertain and report the facts relating to the attack made by Japanese armed forces upon the Territory of Hawaii on December 7, 1941, and to make such recommendations as it may deem proper." The board held sessions beginning July 20, 1944, and concluded its investigation on October 20, 1944. The record of its proceedings and exhibits covers 3,357 printed pages. Members of the board were Lt. Gen. George Grunert, president; Maj. Gen. Henry D. Russell and Maj. Gen. Walter A. Frank.

The Navy Court of Inquiry

The Navy Court of Inquiry was appointed pursuant to the provisions of Public Law 339, Seventy-eighth Congress, approved June 13, 1944, and by order dated July 13, 1944, of the Secretary of the Navy James Forrestal. The court was ordered to thoroughly "inquire into the attack made by Japanese armed forces on Pearl Harbor, Territory of Hawaii, on 7 December 1941 . . . and will include in its findings a full statement of the facts it may deem to be established. The court will further give its opinion as to whether any offenses have been committed or serious blame incurred on the part of any person or persons in the naval service, and in case its opinion be that offenses have been committed or serious blame incurred, will specifically recommend what further proceedings should be had." The court held sessions beginning July 24, 1944, and concluded its inquiry on October 19, 1944. The record of its proceedings and exhibits covers 1,397 printed pages. Members of the court were Admiral Orin G. Murfin, retired, president; Admiral Edward C.

Kalbfus, retired, and Vice Adm. Adolphus Andrews, retired.

The Clarke Inquiry

The investigation conducted by Col. Carter W. Clarke regarding the manner in which certain Top Secret communications were handled "was pursuant to oral instructions of Gen. George C. Marshall, Chief of Staff, United States Army." Colonel Clarke was appointed by Maj. Gen. Clayton Bissell, Chief of the Military Intelligence Division, War Department, under authority of a letter dated September 9, 1944, from The Adjutant General. This investigation was conducted from September 14 to 16, 1944, and from July 13 to August 4, 1945. Testimony was taken concerning the handling of intercepted Japanese messages known as Magic, the handling of intelligence material by the Military Intelligence Division, War Department and the handling of the message sent by General Marshall to Lt. Gen. Walter C. Short at Hawaii on the morning of December 7, 1941. The record of the proceedings of this investigation, together with its exhibits, covers 225 printed pages.

The Clausen Investigation

Secretary of War Henry L. Stimson announced on December 1, 1944, that the report of the Army Pearl Harbor board had been submitted to him, and that: "In accordance with the opinion of the Judge Advocate General, I have decided that my own investigation should be further continued until all the facts are made as clean as possible and until the testimony of every witness in possession of material facts can be obtained and I have given the necessary directions to accomplish this result." By memorandum dated February 6, 1945, for Army personnel concerned, Secretary Stimson stated that "Pursuant to my directions and in accordance with my public statement of 1 December 1944, Major Henry C. Clausen, JAGD, is conducting for me the investigation supplementary to the proceedings of the Army Pearl Harbor Board." This investigation was commenced on November 23, 1944, and was concluded on September 12, 1945. The record of its proceedings and exhibits covers 695 printed pages.

The Hewlitt Inquiry

The inquiry conducted by Admiral H. Kent Hewlitt, United States Navy, was initiated under precept dated May 2, 1945, from Secretary of the Navy James Forrestal to conduct "further investigation of facts pertinent to the Japanese attack on Pearl Harbor, Territory of Hawaii, on 7 December 1941." The precept stated that upon review of the evidence obtained by the examinations conducted by Admiral Thomas C. Hart and by the Navy Court of Inquiry, "the Secretary (of the Navy) has found that there were errors of judgment on the part of certain officers in the Naval Service, both at Pearl Harbor and at Washington. The Secretary has further found that the previous investigations have not exhausted all possible evidence. Accordingly he has decided that the investigation directed by Public Law 339 of the 78th Congress should be further continued until the testimony of every witness in possession of material facts can be obtained and all possible evidence exhausted. . . . You are hereby detailed to make a study of the enclosures (Proceedings of Hart Inquiry and Navy Court of Inquiry) and then to conduct such further investigation, including the examination of any additional persons who may have knowledge of the facts pertinent to the said Japanese attack, to reexamine any such person who has been previously examined, as may appear necessary, and to record the testimony given thereby." This inquiry commenced on May 14, 1945, and was concluded on July 11, 1945. The record of its proceedings and exhibits covers 1,342 printed pages.

Bibliography

Baker, Leonard. *Roosevelt and Pearl Harbor*. New York: Macmillan, 1970.

Barker, A. J. *Pearl Harbor*. New York: Ballantine Books, 1969.

Barnes, Harry Elmer. *Pearl Harbor After a Quarter of a Century*. New York: Arno Press, 1972.

Beard, Charles A. *President Roosevelt and the Coming of the War 1941*. New Haven: Yale University Press, 1948.

Borg, Dorothy. *Pearl Harbor as History*. New York: Columbia University Press, 1976.

Burns, James McGregor. *Roosevelt: The Lion and the Fox*. New York: Harcourt, Brace, and Company, 1956.

Butow, Robert J. C. *Tojo and the Coming of the War*. Princeton, N.J.: Princeton University Press, 1961.

Butow, Robert J. C. *John Doe and Associates*. Stanford, Calif.: Stanford University Press, 1974.

Davis, Forrest and Lindley, Ernest K. *How War Came*. New York: Simon and Schuster, 1942.

Dilts, Marion May. *The Pageant of Japanese History*. New York: Longmans, Green, and Company, 1961.

Farago, Ladislas. *The Broken Seal*. New York: Random House, 1967.

Feis, Herbert. *The Road to Pearl Harbor*. Princeton, N.J.: Princeton University Press, 1950.

Foreign Relations of the United States: Japan, 1931–1941. Vols. I and II. Washington: U.S. Government Printing Office, 1943.

Foreign Relations of the United States: Diplomatic Papers, 1931 et supra. Washington: U.S. Government Printing Office.

Grew, Joseph C. *Ten Years in Japan*. New York: Simon and Schuster, 1944.

Grew, Joseph C. *Turbulent Era*. Boston: Houghton Mifflin Company, 1952.

Halsey, William F. *Admiral Halsey's Story*. New York: McGraw-Hill Book Company, Inc., 1947.

Hoehling, Adolph A. *The Week Before Pearl Harbor*. New York: W. W. Norton and Company, Inc., 1963.

Kimmel, Husband E. *Admiral Kimmel's Story*. Chicago: Henry Regnery Company, Inc., 1955.

Kurusu, Saburo. *Treacherous America*. Tokyo: Japan Times, 1942.

Lord, Walter. *Day of Infamy*. New York: Henry Holt and Company, 1957.

Millis, Walter. *This Is Pearl!* New York: W. Morrow and Company, Inc., 1947.

Morgenstern, George. *Pearl Harbor: The Story of the Secret War*. New York: The Devin-Adair Company, 1947.

Morison, Samuel Eliot. *The Rising Sun in the*

Pacific, 1931–April 1942. Boston: Little Brown and Company, 1954.

Parkinson, Roger. *Attack on Pearl Harbor.* London: Wayland, 1973.

Pearl Harbor Attack, Hearings of the Seventy-ninth Congress, First and Second Sessions;
Pursuant to S. Con. Res. 27. 39 volumes. Reprint of 1946 ed. New York: AMS Press, 1972. Contents: Vols. 1–11 Hearings Nov. 15, 1945–May 31, 1946; Vols. 12–21 Joint Committee Exhibits No. 1–183; Vols. 22–25 Proceedings of Roberts Commission; Vol. 26 Proceedings of Hart Inquiry; Vols. 27–31 Proceedings of Army Pearl Harbor Board; Vols. 32–33 Proceedings of Clausen Investigation; Vols. 36–38 Proceedings of Hewitt Inquiry; Vol. 39 Reports Findings, and Conclusions of Roberts Commission, Army Pearl Harbor Board, Navy Court of Inquiry, and Hewitt Inquiry, with endorsements.

Peace and War: United States Foreign Policy 1931–1941. Washington: U.S. Government Printing Office, 1943.

Pogue, Forrest C. *George C. Marshall: The War Years.* New York: The Viking Press, 1965.

Tansill, Charles C. *Back Door to War: The Roosevelt Foreign Policy, 1933–1941.* Chicago: Henry Regnery Company, 1952.

Theobald, Robert A. *The Final Secret of Pearl Harbor.* New York: The Devin-Adair Company, 1954.

Tiedmann, Arthur. *Modern Japan.* Princeton, N.J.: D. Van Nostrand Company, Inc., 1955.

Trefousse, Hans L. (Ed.) *What Happened at Pearl Harbor.* New York: Twayne Publishers, 1958.

Waller, George McGregor. *Pearl Harbor: Roosevelt and the Coming of the War.* Boston: D. C. Heath and Company, 1953.

Whitehead, Don. *The FBI Story.* New York: Random House, 1956.

Wohlstetter, Roberta. *Pearl Harbor; Warning and Decision.* Stanford, Calif.: Stanford University Press, 1962.

Source documents were examined at:

Japanese Foreign Office, Tokyo, Japan.
Library of Congress, Washington, D.C.
Martin Luther King, Jr. Memorial Library,
National Archives, Washington, D.C.
Navy Historical Office, Washington, D.C.
  Washington, D.C.
New York Public Library, New York, N.Y.
Peruvian Foreign Office, Lima, Peru.
Roosevelt Library, Hyde Park, N.Y.
Tokyo Public Library, Tokyo, Japan.
Truman Library, Independence, Mo.
Washington National Records Center, Suitland, Maryland.

APPENDIX B

AUTHORS' NOTE:

Since passage of the Freedom of Information Act, whole new sources of data are available to researchers. In gathering documentation, we uncovered thousands of pieces of communications that support the contentions we have expressed. Probably the most dramatic evidence is in the obvious awareness of mysterious Japanese activities during the year leading up to the attack on Pearl Harbor. Despite the overwhelming mass of indicators, the "Peace-Is-Possible" faction within the Department of State prevailed. Hornbeck, Hamilton, Ballantine, and Grew were able to override the frustrations of the Federal Bureau of Investigation and other intelligence sources and, as history so sadly records, the leaders of our nation were lulled into a nearly fatal sense of hope. A small sample of official memos and communications follows.

(Authors' comment on May 15 memo: The meeting was rumored to be about the Sino-Japanese Peace Pact but history shows it was more than peace in light of the "escort" and "convoy" references.)

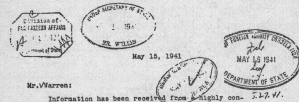

May 15, 1941

701.9411/1401

101.9411

Mr. Warren:

Information has been received from a highly confidential source that during the past week-end Consular
Officers of the Japanese Government were called to
Washington for a very unusual conference. None of the
American employees of the Embassy knew that this conference was going on until they arrived for duty Monday
morning at which time they discovered the Embassy had
been completely turned upside down. Typewriters which
had formerly been used by the American clerical employees
were being used by Japanese in a locked room. These
American employees were informed that this matter was
strictly confidential and they were told to ask no questions whatsoever. They were also warned not to attempt
to observe any matter that was being handled at the Embassy on that date. It is reported that one of the
Embassy's Japanese employees advised some of the American
employees that they were busy writing the Sino-Japanese
peace pact. It is believed that this statement was made
merely to mislead the Americans. It is also known that
one of the Japanese employees on this date was interested
in obtaining an explanation as to the difference in meaning of the words "escort" and "convoy". The opinion has
been

243

been voiced that the Japanese/has possibly obtained an
advanced copy of the President's speech that was to have
been made this week.

It has also been ascertained that the German butler,
Mr. Strievy, who was supposed to have been discharged
during the past week, was back at the Embassy on the morning during which the above-mentioned activity took place.
It was reported that he was sitting in on various con-
ferences and was in apparent close collaboration with the
Japanese Ambassador. All the American employees of the
Japanese Embassy are reported to have stated that such
activity has not been carried on in the Embassy in the
past twenty-five years.

FC: fcof
        3/.

(Authors' comment on July 24 memo: The overt act of evacuation speaks for itself and, considering that negotiations were "hopeful" at that time, it is obvious that a decision had been made.)

TEM   Pretoria
This telegram must be
closely paraphrased be-   Dated July 24, 1941
fore being communicated
to anyone. (br)   Rec'd 6:25 p.m.

FROM

Secretary of State
Washington

73, July 24, 5 p.m.

All Japanese residents in the Union of South
Africa except male members of the diplomatic and
consular corps are being evacuated to Japan this
week on the steamship MANILA MARU now at Capetown.
Except for the Japanese freighter BELGIUM MARU now
at Durban this will be the last Japanese vessel to
visit South Africa for an indefinite period.

The manager of Barclays Bank informed me that
liquidation and transfer of Japanese assets in
South Africa, which have been proceeding for some
time, are now as complete as the exchange regulations
will permit it.

KEENA

WSB

246

DCR: Please teletype to Navy
under confidential classifi-
cation, endorse sending time
and return to U-L, Room 185.

FROM STATE DEPARTMENT FOR OPNAV:

Following received 7-24-41, 6:25 p.m.   from

Pretoria   dated   7-24-41, 5 p.m.   8

No. 73.

The MANILA MARU is carrying to Japan this week all residents
of Japan in the Union of South Africa save the male personnel of
the consular and diplomatic corps. This steamer is now at Capetown.
The MANILA MARU will be the last Japanese ship to visit South Africa
for an indefinite period except for the BELGIUM MARU, a Japanese
freighter which is now at Durban. I have been told by the manager
of Barclays Bank that the transfer and liquidation of assets of
Japan in the Union of South Africa, which have been in progres for
quite a while, are now as fully realized as regulations of the exchange will allow.

KEENA

U-L:EMA
Teletyped to OPNAV, 7-25-41.
Confirmation copy to NAVY, 7-25-41.

(Authors' comment on August 11 memo: While Yamamoto was getting his attack fleet ready, Japanese diplomats began their preparations for war by lowering their exposure in the United States.)

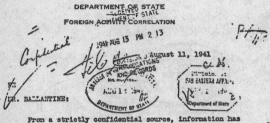

DEPARTMENT OF STATE
FOREIGN ACTIVITY CORRELATION

August 11, 1941

MR. BALLANTINE:

From a strictly confidential source, information has
been received to the effect that the Japanese Military
Attache's office will be moved from 2032 Belmont Road to
the Japanese Embassy within the next two weeks.

Information has been received indicating that the
Japanese Naval Inspector's office in New York was officially
closed as of August 7. One man will be left in charge of
the office until the lease expires on August 31.

This New York office has been systematically withdrawing
its staff. For the past two weeks they have been destroying
their records. Those records that are to be retained have
been transferred to the office of the Japanese Consul General
in New York.

F. B. Lyon

FC:FBL:GS

TREASURY DEPARTMENT

Washington.

ASSISTANT SECRETARY

December 19, 1941.

Honorable Breckinridge Long,
Assistant Secretary of State,
Washington, D.C.

Dear Mr. Long:

I don't know whether or not information such as the enclosed has any record interest to the State Department, but at least I think you may be interested. The clipping was sent in by a Treasury man in Canada.

Very truly yours,

Herbert E. Gaston
Assistant Secretary of the Treasury.

Enclosure

740.0011 PACIFIC WAR/1400

PS/ATB

JAN 8 1942

(Authors' comment on November 25 letter: Possibly a coincidence, but a curious one, on the part of a high-level Japanese diplomat.)

November 25, 1941

Dear Sir:

Referring to the booklet which you
were so kind as to send to me at my request,
I wish to have the articles of the annexed
list delivered to me. I should like to have
them before December 7th at the latest. As
regards the payment, I will be much obliged
if you will designate an agent in Washington,
D.C. (or in New York) to whom I may be able to
pay in cash; this may save me from encountering many technical difficulties of transfer of
funds under the freezing order.

I may add that the delivery of the
commodities to me will be effected duty free
at the American border. I must, however,
notify the State Department beforehand and
for that purpose I ask you to inform me of the
approximate date of the passage of the goods.

Yours sincerely,

Koto Matsudaira,
First Secretary.

Mr. Herbert S. Mills
Hamilton (Ontario)
Canada

(Authors' comment on December 3 letter and report: Hoover reports findings by use of an FBI telephone tap on the Japanese Embassy. "The child is about to be born . . ." refers to the Imperial Council's, under the Emperor's authority, decision to initiate a war with the U.S. that was made December 2nd. "Selling the mountain . . ."—we now know—referred to the Japanese code phrase "Climb Mount Niitaka" as launch instructions to the attack fleet going against Pearl Harbor.)

402

Federal Bureau of Investigation
United States Department of Justice
Washington, D. C.

December 3, 1941

PERSONAL AND
CONFIDENTIAL

Honorable Adolf A. Berle, Jr.
Assistant Secretary of State
Department of State
Washington, D. C.

DEC 5 - 1941
MR. BERLE

Division of
FAR EASTERN AFFAIRS
DEC 10 1941
Department of State

Dear Mr. Berle:

It has been learned by this Bureau through a highly confidential source that Mr. Saburo Kurusu, special envoy of the Japanese Government in Washington, D. C., communicated several times by telephone with one Yamamoto in Tokyo on November 27, 1941. It is believed that Yamamoto is Kumaichi Yamamoto of the Japanese Foreign Office.

The translation from the Japanese of one of these conversations and a summary translation of another call are enclosed.

As you will note, the exact nature of the conversations is not clearly intelligible, but it is believed that even in their present form they may be of significant interest to you in connection with the present discussions being had between representatives of the United States and Japan.

Sincerely yours,

J. Edgar Hoover

Enclosure

BY SPECIAL
MESSENGER

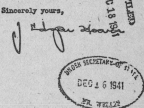

UNDER SECRETARY OF STATE
DEC 16 1941
MR. WELLS

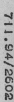

711.94/2602

PS/AML

254

EXCERPTS FROM TRANSLATION
OF CONVERSATION MONITORED
NOVEMBER 27, 1941

Y. "We are anxious about that matter."

K. "Yes, yes. Now? A problem? Now the problem is the one concerning the neighbor. Concerning the neighbor, do you understand?"

Y. "Yes, yes."

K. "The movement in the neighboring country. They have heard about it."

Y. "Yes, yes."

K. "Regarding the trade problem, they are making a lot of noise about it, and concerning the Southern push, they understand all about it."

Y. "Ah, ah, eh."

K. "Then?"

Y. "Yes."

K. "It has become like that in this country."

Y. "Yes, yes."

K. "Yes. Then it is a problem, isn't it?"

Y. "Yes, yes."

K. "Ah, ah (he laughs slightly). Therefore."

Y. "Yes."

K. "We have all made various explanations."

Y. "Yes, yes."

K. "Well then in regard to going South, they understand everything."

Y. "I see."

K. "Look at the cablegram."

Y. "Has it been sent?"

K. "Yes."

Y. "Is that so."

K. "Please look again at what is contained in it."

Y. "Yes, the telegram has gone."

K. "Ah, is that so?"

Y. "It is a long (telegram?) so study it well."

K. "Yes."

Y. "Look at it carefully."

K. "Yes."

Y. "You understand that, don't you?"

K. "In regard to that question."

Y. "Who?"

K. "Kimiko."

Y. "Kimiko is going Friday."

K. "She is going to the country on Friday?"

Y. "Yes."

K. "Starting on Friday?"

Y. "She is going to the country on Friday."

K. "Yes, yes."

Y. "She is not going very far into the country."

Y. "Just wait a minute."

(Interval)

(K waits.)

Y. "Hello, hello."

K. "Yes, yes."

Y. "A child is about to be born (rest unintelligible)—"

K. "What is it?"

Y. "There are too many children."

K. "Yes."

Y. "Very—" (Kurusu interrupts)

K. "I think that may be so, a child will be born."

Y. "Yes?"

K. (He laughs here.)

Y. "So—about to be born."

K. "Because here a child is about to be born. He laughs) That is the intention. That's the intention, isn't it?"

Y. "Yes."

K. "I can't be sure about it, but—"

Y. "Yes."

K. "Well at any rate, it may be well to continue the negotiations."

Y. "Yes."

K. "That's all."

Y. "Ah, is that so."

258

K. "At any rate the other side (the U.S.) certainly has strength, and for that reason, it will be necessary to wash the face."

Y. "Ha, ha, ha!"

K. "Yes."

Y. "Then New York and—San Francisco—"

K. "That's all in regard to these questions."

Y. "Yes."

K. "In that case the whole matter goes back to what it was originally."

Y. "Yes, that's so."

SUMMARY TRANSLATION

Yamamoto calls Kurusu from Tokyo and asks how negotiations are getting along. Kurusu expresses surprise that he has not gotten the telegram that left about six or seven (i.e. about three hours previous to the call). It hasn't changed much from the story of "broadminded Umeko." Also, the thing we talked about yesterday, about the South, a great deal of it has gotten out. It looks like negotiations will be postponed (or prolonged). There are other things but that is the chief one. The telegram ought to come soon and tell it in detail. It is not long so you should be able to read it quickly.

Then Kurusu seems to break the subject. He asks if a baby is about to be born, and WHETHER IT SEEMS TO BE a boy or a girl. Yamamoto says it *seems* to be a healthy boy.

Yamamoto goes on to ask if there has been any development on point "A." Kurusu replies, "No, they have merely met." Yamamoto says that points in the telegram a while ago have not been completed but point "A" is very difficult. Kurusu replies that in that case things are at a standstill. Yamamoto goes on to say, "Let Yoshizawa know about these things."

Kurusu says to be sure to read carefully the place about Kimiko.

Yamamoto asks about the time of today's conference and is told it began about two-thirty and lasted about an hour.

Yamamoto says to telegraph him if negotiations come to an end, and makes some complaint (substance was unintelligible) about the last telegram. Kurusu replies that it is hard to negotiate over nothing. The other side wants to tie us down, and we keep making a fuss about a child being born and Tokugawa being a great man. So it won't come to anything.

Yamamoto says, "We won't sell the mountain," and Kurusu says, "That is understood. There is no question about it."

Yamamoto repeats his previous statement about the mountain and then says the news about Manchuria came in the telegram and "I pass it on to you," or "Desperate factors—march on Manchuria." (Translater's Note: The sounds are very hard to distinguish at this point and it may well be that neither of these statements is correct.)

Kurusu says Kimoko is going to the country tomorrow to stay till Wednesday.

Yamamoto says that whichever way it turns out he wants Kurusu to do his best and Kurusu replies that he and Nomura are both doing that.

Yamamoto asks if anything special has suddenly developed and is told, no, but a great deal has come out about the Southern affair.

(Translator's Note: The translator has reason to feel that there is more involved in the words "baby is born," "sell the mountain," and the girl's name "Kimiko," than appears on the surface.)

(Authors' comment on December 5 letter: The FBI was getting too many strong vibrations from their secret telephone tap lines. Hoover's frustration was building.)

JOHN EDGAR HOOVER
DIRECTOR

Federal Bureau of Investigation
United States Department of Justice
Washington, D. C.

December 5, 1941

PERSONAL AND CONFIDENTIAL
SPECIAL MESSENGER

Honorable Adolf A. Berle, Jr.
Assistant Secretary of State
Department of State
Washington, D. C.

DEC 6 - 1941
MR. BERLE

My dear Mr. Berle:

Information has come to the attention of this Bureau
through a highly confidential source indicating that on
December 1, 1941, Shigeo Kobata of the Japanese Embassy,
Washington, D. C., contacted a woman named Kinoshita in San
Francisco, California, and advised her that the efforts of the
Embassy were failing and all of the staff were getting ready
to leave within twenty-four hours, although all of the officials
were not going back to Japan. Kobata allegedly asserted that he
had been given the choice of staying in the United States or
going to either Mexico or Argentina and seemed unable to make up
his mind as to which he would accept.

Kinoshita reportedly inquired that if American-
Japanese relations were broken and the Embassy was closed how
long the resultant condition would last. She commented that
the opinion of people in San Francisco was that the war would
probably last two years. However, Kobata supposedly expressed
the opinion that it would last longer.

It has also been reported that Kobata mentioned something about employees of the Embassy being placed in a concentration camp in the event of war, although he assured Kinoshita
that "other people have nothing to worry about."

This information is being submitted as a matter of
interest to you.

Sincerely yours,

J. E. Hoover

DIV. OF FOREIGN ACTIVITY CORRELATION
DEC 6 1941
DEPARTMENT OF STATE

740.0011 P. W./9.17   PS/GD

264

DEPARTMENT OF STATE

FOREIGN ACTIVITY CORRELATION

December 9, 1941

Mr. Warren:

Mr. Laughlin of F.B.I. called and gave me the following message for you:

The Bureau has learned that the Washington Embassy advised the Japanese Consulate in New York on December 7 that they received a telegram from Tokyo, the contents of which could not be disclosed. The Embassy officials also made inquiry as to whether members of the New York Consulate had sufficient money available and advised that all the tickets for the Tatuta Maru have now been given out.

mf

(Authors' comment on December 6 letter: From the experience of Pearl Harbor, such intelligence has come to be virtually considered a declaration of war.)

DEC 11 1941   December 8, 1941

Mr. Warren:

Commander Davis of ONI called and said that he
has received information that the Japanese Embassy
burned its secret codes and ciphers yesterday.

nf
mf

701.94n/1532 1/2

701.94n/1532 1/2

FTL.RET.
JAN 12 1942

267

(Authors' comment on November 18, 1941 memorandum: Probably one of the most brazen considerations ever undertaken by our Federal Government: giving away another nation's property. Time ran out but, very possibly, this brainchild of Hornbeck and Hamilton might have been initiated.)

DEPARTMENT OF STATE

SPECIAL ASSISTANT TO THE SECRETARY

February 5, 1946

According to the recollection of
the undersigned, no action was taken
on the attached memorandum to Secretary
Hull dated November 18, 1941, concerning which Senator Ferguson inquired
(Pearl Harbor Committee Hearings,
January 21, 1946, pages 7868, 7869).

We have consulted Mr. Hull who,
according to his best recollection,
confirms that no action was taken on
the memorandum in question and believes
that it did not reach the President.

M. M. H. — J W. B.

DEPARTMENT OF STATE
DIVISION OF FAR EASTERN AFFAIRS

November 19, 1941.

STRICTLY CONFIDENTIAL

NOV 25 1941 NOTED

Mr. Secretary:

Herewith another idea which might possibly be of constructive value in your discussions with the Japanese Ambassador. The proposal might cause Japan to feel that she was being given sufficient "face" to enable her to agree in good faith to remove all her troops from China.

At first blush the proposal may appear to represent "appeasement". However, Japan would under the proposal sell to the United States ships which we very much need. Also, the sale by Japan of such ships to us at this time would mean a very practical step by Japan away from her Axis alliance with Germany.

The Australians and the Dutch would be perturbed by such a proposal, especially at first glance. However, it is also to their interest that additional shipping be made available to us and that Japan's offensive striking power be lessened.

We would of course have to discuss this with the Australians and the British (and the Dutch if their territory should be involved) before making any mention of the proposal to the Japanese.

I send this forward in the light of your request that we explore all possibilities.

FE:MMH:HES

DEPARTMENT OF STATE
———
DIVISION OF FAR EASTERN AFFAIRS

CONFIDENTIAL

November 17, 1941.

PROPOSAL FOR THE EXCHANGE OF CERTAIN TERRITORIES
IN THE PACIFIC FOR JAPANESE SHIPS

Agreement might be reached between the United
States and Japan (with the assent of the other countries concerned) along the following lines:

I. Japan to purchase New Guinea.

    1. The western part (belonging to the
       Netherlands)

              or

    2. The southeastern part (Papua) (under the
       Government of Australia)

              or

    3. The northeastern part (now administered by
       Australia under a mandate from the League
       of Nations). (The mandate for this terri-
       tory might be transferred to Japan, Au-
       stralia being compensated for a relinquish-
       ment of its rights by Japan.)

              or

    All three.

II. The United States to furnish funds to Japan
for the purchase of these territories.

                             III.

III. Japan to reimburse the United States through the transfer to this Government of merchant ships or possibly certain categories of naval vessels.

Such an arrangement would of course be reached only in conjunction with an agreement on the part of Japan to withdraw its forces from China and to follow general courses of peace.

Note in regard to the mandated territory of New Guinea: Neither the Covenant of the League of Nations nor the text of the Mandate for New Guinea contains any provision with regard to the manner of revocation of a Mandate or the transfer of a Mandate from one mandatory to another. The Mandate for New Guinea provides, however, that the Mandate may be modified with the consent of the Council so it would seem that the Mandate might be transferred in like manner by the Council with the consent of the mandatory. The Council is now in suspension, but if desired a special session could probably be convened. Alternatively, it would seem that the mandate might be transferred -- or sovereignty over the territory might actually be vested in Japan -- by the Principal Allied and Associated Powers -- that is, the United States, the British Empire, France, Italy, and Japan -- these powers having conferred the Mandate for New Guinea upon Australia.

(Authors' comment on January 28, 1942 memo (referring to December 5, 1941): Terasaki, acknowledged as the top Japanese spy in the Western Hemisphere, is about to slip out of the country right before the attack on Pearl Harbor.)

January 28, 1942.

Mr. Secretary:
This may interest you: it merely
illustrates some of the work
of the Division, which is not
well known - and ought not
to be -
aas

May I set forth the following information with
regard to a group of five Japanese who left the United
States on the evening of December 5, 1941, aboard the
S.S. Brazil of the American Republics Line for destina-
tions in South America?

During the first week of December 1941 FC was much
concerned about the planned departure of a considerable
number of Japanese officials and their families from
this country to South America. The question was raised
whether it would not be possible to request the other
American republics to refuse to accept them on the ground
of their being personae non gratae. However, it was not
deemed advisable to do this. FC was particularly concerned because it appeared that Mr. Hidenari Terasaki,
First Secretary of the Japanese Embassy, whom the investigative agencies of this Government consider to be the
head of the Japanese espionage system in the United States,
was departing for Rio de Janeiro. It looked as though

Terasaki

274

Terasaki was going to Rio de Janeiro to set up there
the espionage system which had been carried on in this
country and which had to be discontinued in case of war.
VD and FC were unable to find any grounds on which to
prevent the departure of these persons for South America,
although more than fifty exit visas were granted by the
Visa Division before war came. Included in this number
were five issued to Consul Hirawasa and his wife and
three members of the staff of the Japanese Embassy in
Washington; Hiroichi Takagi, Shigeto Nikai and Rynichi
Anao. These five persons actually sailed aboard the
S.S. Brazil on the night of December 5, 1941 for Rio de
Janeiro and Buenos Aires.

After the attack on Pearl Harbor, it occurred to FC
that it would be desirable to stop these five Japanese
at some port on their trip south. The matter was put
up to you and you authorized that the endeavor be made.
Through the British Embassy here the assistance of London
was enlisted in obtaining the cooperation of the British
authorities at Barbados in the removal of these five
persons from the S.S. Brazil upon its call at that island.
The Barbados authorities cooperated fully and the five
persons were removed when the vessel reached that port.

It

-3-

It was clearly understood by the British that these
Japanese must be returned to the United States. The
British authorities then transported them to Trinidad,
where they were questioned and placed aboard the
S.S. Lady Drake for return to this country.

During the trip north these five persons were again
questioned by the British officials aboard the Lady Drake.
The ship did not put in at Boston but proceeded to
St. Johns and to Halifax. Upon the arrival of the vessel at Halifax, officers of the United States Federal
Bureau of Investigation cooperated with the British in
another examination of the Japanese. When the S.S. Lady
Drake left Halifax on its southbound voyage it called
at Boston and disembarked the five Japanese. At Boston
they were taken into custody by representatives of the
Immigration and Naturalization Service and were
accompanied by them and Special Agents of the Department
of State to the Homestead Hotel at Hot Springs, Virginia.
They are now detained at the Homestead.

In their examination of the Japanese, the British
discovered in the possession of one of the officers a
trunk belonging to Assistant Naval Attaché Lieutenant
Commander Yoshimori Terai, who was then and is now

                              detained

276

-4-

detained at the Homestead. This trunk, the British
reported, contained several maps which revealed
important American naval information. The Japanese
official in whose possession the trunk was found stated
that the maps belonged to Lieutenant Commander Terai
and that he had taken the trunk at Lieutenant Commander
Terai's express request and upon his assurance that it
only contained books and other publications entirely
unobjectionable. The Lieutenant Commander stated that
he would later come to South America by plane and
requested that the officer in question take the trunk
as a part of his own steamer baggage in order to save
the Assistant Naval Attaché the cost and trouble of
shipping it by air.

The British considered the information obtained of
great importance. Of course, it is being made available
to our investigative agencies.

Fletcher Warren

Pinnacle Books proudly presents

A BICENTENNIAL CLASSICS SERIES

Starting with four great American historical novels by Bruce Lancaster, one of America's most distinguished historians.

_____TRUMPET TO ARMS An exceptionally crafted romance spun beautifully amidst the fury of the American Revolution. (PB-887, 1.75)
"Explosive in style . . . *Trumpet to Arms* is always easy to read and strikes a note as stirring as a call to battle."
—*The Boston Globe*

_____THE SECRET ROAD A fascinating, yet little known account of the exploits of Washington's Secret Service. A gripping story of America's first espionage unit. (PB-889, 1.75)
"A veteran craftsman at the top of his form."
—*The New York Times*

_____PHANTOM FORTRESS A masterful treatment of the career of General Francis Marion, known to history as "The Swamp Fox." (PB-905, 1.75)
"History that is good and galloping, for competent scholarship underlies the romantic story."
—*New York Herald Tribune*

_____BLIND JOURNEY An absorbing tale of romance and adventure that moves from 18th-century France and its grandeur to the carnage of revolutionary America. A story no one should miss. (PB-915, 1.75)
"Romance, adventure . . . full pulsing life. Bruce Lancaster's best."

—*The Boston Herald*

Check which books you want. If you can't find any of these books at your local bookstore, simply send the cover price plus 25¢ per book for postage and handling to us and we'll mail you your book(s).

PINNACLE BOOKS
275 Madison Avenue, New York, New York 10016

PB-32